Wounded Spirits

Wounded Spirits

LESLIE D. WEATHERHEAD

"The spirit of a man will sustain his infirmity;
but a wounded spirit who can raise up?"
—THE BOOK OF PROVERBS

How sweet the name of Jesus sounds
  In a believer's ear!
It soothes his sorrows, heals his wounds,
  And drives away his fear.

It makes the wounded spirit whole, . . .
—JOHN NEWTON, 1725-1807

ABINGDON PRESS NEW YORK NASHVILLE

WOUNDED SPIRITS

Library of Congress Catalog Card Number: 63-10563

Scripture quotations unless otherwise noted are
from the American Standard Version of the Bible.

SET UP, PRINTED, AND BOUND BY THE
PARTHENON PRESS, AT NASHVILLE,
TENNESSEE, UNITED STATES OF AMERICA

FOR

Ingrid and Kingsley

GREATLY BELOVED

PREFACE

THIS BOOK, WHICH IN SOME SENSE COULD BE REGARDED AS A footnote to an earlier treatise called *Psychology, Religion and Healing*, is a true account of the way in which certain people known to me found their way back to a measure of health. Their cases were so unusual that they are worth recording. I have given them different names, of course, since at the moment of writing they are all alive and, with one exception,[1] well. Where the novelist prefaces his book with the declaration, "The characters in this book are entirely imaginary and bear no relation to living people. Any resemblance is purely coincidental," I have to say that the characters in my book are all living people, but I have altered unimportant details so that the reader will not be able easily to identify them. The names are wholly imaginary. Where letters are quoted, they have not been altered save where names occur. Where there is risk of identification, or where an unaccustomed reader might be incredulous, I have, where possible, asked the one-

[1] Bert Abbott (pp. 139 ff.).

time patient or his parents to read through the account of his experiences and suggest any alterations he may care to make, and to give me permission to publish, as psychologically accurate, what you will read herein. I ought to apologize for using the word "patient," for the word is the copyright of the medical profession. Yet although people call themselves "sheep" every Sunday, and a pastor talks of his "flock," it would seem odd, and might be resented, if I called the people I have tried to help "sheep." Imagine writing, "This sheep presented most interesting symptoms!"

I am aware, of course, that some of the healings recorded in this book are "unorthodox" from the standpoint of the general practitioner, the psychotherapist, or even the so-called faith healer. I include them just because they are unusual and because I am a seeker for truth and have been interested for forty years in healing by nonphysical methods. If a patient can be *permanently* restored to health, then, whatever the method may have been, our first reaction should be joy and gladness, not a carping, critical attitude. I underline the word "permanently" because of the sickening way—justifying very severe criticism—in which some so-called healers rush into newspaper headlines, advertising a "cure" without any understanding that certain emotional conditions can easily banish a symptom for a short period or permanently set up an alternative symptom far more difficult to cure.

Our second reaction should be to try to understand exactly what caused the illness and why the methods used brought about cure. Then cautiously, and without promising too much or using the word "cured" too early, we should try to bring such a treatment as helped one patient to the aid of another, eliminating anything discoverably false either in the technique used or in the philosophy lying behind it, and resolutely avoiding exaggerated and highly colored language.

Many varieties of treatment, I believe, will open up to us as we discover more about the nature of man and the universe in which he is called upon to live. Concerning the material part of the universe and the laws which operate within it, we have made impressive progress. But all around us are vast areas all but unknown. In and through them immense energies seem to operate. We catch a glimpse of them at work when an "incurable" invalid who has been ill all his life and usually in great pain—an invalid, moreover, who has no faith in, or love for, God or man—turns on his radio one Sunday morning, hears a sermon, and forthwith gets up from his bed never to return to it for reasons of illness again,[2] or when a child, who has been given up by eminent consultants and whose mother is sitting at his bedside waiting for him to die, is prayed for in a church several hundred miles away from his bed by people who have never heard of him, and begins to make a recovery from which he never looks back.[3] Some stories in this book give us similar glimpses of these energies. But we need to go farther, to understand them, to find out the laws which lie behind them, to be able to release them instead of merely marveling at their sporadic incidence and, more frequently, grieving at our failure to rely on their potency in a crisis.

There is a vast field of inquiry vaguely labeled "psychic research." We know little about it. The Spiritualists—who in my opinion have proved their case; that is to say they have

[2] I have described such a case in Appendix 4, *Psychology, Religion and Healing*, and have since met the patient. (Rev. ed.; Nashville: Abingdon Press, 1951, 1952.)

[3] See Appendix 3, *Psychology, Religion and Healing*, and chap. 12 of this book.

9

proved that in certain cases contact with the so-called dead is possible—sometimes try to prove too much. In my view they accept the spiritualistic explanation when the "law of parsimony" indicates a simpler explanation.[4] For this and other reasons, scientists in other fields hold them in the main as suspect and will rarely devote to psychic matters the attention they deserve. Yet my own hunch is that serious science will soon turn to this difficult and hilly country and will then find its exploration rewarding in many fields of human thought, especially that of the nonmaterial part of man's nature, and thus of new ways of healing many of his illnesses through a new understanding of what man is.

Even more important is the vast field which we could label "spiritual." Prayer works according to law, as does everything else in a universe which is cosmos everywhere and chaos nowhere. We pray without knowledge or insight, with a kind of hopeful unexpectancy, a hit-or-miss attitude which results in more misses than hits. We are like the boy angler who, when asked if he had caught any fish, said, "I haven't caught as many as I hoped, but then I didn't expect to." But when Jesus worked his miracles, his attitude was not, "These things I can do, but you may never do them." He was at home in a sphere where miracles are natural events. They strike us as amazing because we are not at home on that plane of relationship with God and men. But it is not entirely closed to us. Our limitations are not his bounds, nor even ultimately our bounds.[5]

[4] The "law of parsimony," formulated by William of Ockham in the fifteenth century, requires that where a simple hypothesis adequately explains all the facts, an alternative hypothesis which is farther removed from natural science should not be resorted to. As William said tersely, "A plurality must not be asserted without necessity."

[5] Dr. W. R. Maltby, The Significance of Jesus (London: S.C.M. Press, 1929), p. 28.

His miracles were signs of the new kingdom; they were characteristic of it.[6] And he has "opened the kingdom of heaven to all believers." I am quite sure that the Christian church, which lost the secret of true spiritual healing by the end of the third century, could recover it through fellowship, prayer, and study. One feels that a spiritual energy far more potent to heal than atomic energy is to destroy, is, as it were, around the corner. Sometimes, almost by accident, we hit on those conditions under which it is released and a "miraculous cure" is reported in the press; but these occasions are only too rare, and even when they happen we learn little from them for the benefit of others.

This book is written to stimulate inquiry and research and co-operation, so that we need not be like men living in penury with an unheard-of fortune in the bank, or men who push wheels around with their hands when within reach is an energy that could drive them with far greater power, or men who watch with fear-stricken hearts the suffering of their fellows when the healing powers of God, in one or another of their manifold expressions, are within their too-reluctant grasp.

"Ye shall receive power, when the Holy Spirit is come upon you: and ye shall be my witnesses." (Acts 1:8.) That Holy Ghost is the Spirit of Truth, himself the Goal of our search, the Urge to seek it, and the Guide toward it. For myself, I want to find out why so many people remain ill; why they fall ill; why some, but not others, recover. I want to find out the truth about sick people. I want to understand.

There is one charge I sincerely hope to avoid: that of an apparent superiority. Doctors must grow sick of reading in newspapers and books of people who were cured of this and

---

[6] See Matt. 11:3 ff.

that "when the doctors could do no more." If the records of any hospital in the land were published, we should all be thrilled by the stories of healings that would be revealed. Some of the cases in this book could have been cured by any psychotherapist, and some by any minister with insight. Some had, in a sense, nothing to do with me at all. My own failures frequently depress me, and I feel very humble when I stand confronted by the immense problem of suffering. All sincere workers in the field of human suffering would agree that we know so little. I honor immensely the medical profession, and value all it has done and is doing. In the mental atmosphere which, as it were, our minds breathe today, I see no future for any healing movement which does not take account of and work with the medical profession. We cannot go back in time and breathe the atmosphere of credulity in which men lived in New Testament days. We should suffocate in it. Science has come to stay, and to pretend otherwise is no service to true religion. What I would like to do is to contribute to a closer co-operation between medicine, psychology, and religion, so that the healing energies in all three fields can be set free to make sick people well.

I must add an expression of gratitude. Once more my wife, who has helped me with over thirty books, has proved herself the kindliest but strictest of critics and the most efficient of proofreaders. Miss W. E. Haddon, who for twenty years was my private secretary at the City Temple, London, typed the first rough draft of some of the following chapters. A large measure of gratitude must go to another friend, Miss Elsie B. Thompson of Bexhill-on-Sea, who retyped the whole book and helped with the proofreading with great patience and efficiency. Without her help I should never have been able to complete it. To all these and to the "patients" who were so willing to co-operate and allow their letters to me to be published, I here tender my warmest thanks. I hope their courage will help other "wounded spirits."

—LESLIE D. WEATHERHEAD

CONTENTS

15

INTRODUCTION [1]

IN STATING THE POINT OF VIEW OF THIS BOOK AND ITS underlying assumptions, I shall assume first of all that the ideal intention of God, God's will—in the only intelligent use of that word—is perfect health of body, mind, and spirit for all his children.

I feel angry as well as sad when some poor soul suffering from some so-called incurable disease is told that his illness is "the will of God." Jesus said that illness was the work of Satan (Luke 13:16) and Paul agreed in the case of his own illness (II Cor. 12:7), and whether by Satan we mean an evil intelligence or a convenient name for the ignorance, folly, and evil in the world does not much matter. God, I am certain, is on the side of the true healer, and when a patient is healed God's will is done. No artist, least of all God, could "will" imperfection in the created object. If, as one eager to promote health, I suspected that God did not really want a sufferer to be well, my work would be mentally sabotaged at the start.

[1] I have reprinted here material which originally appeared in the *Cambridge University Medical Society Magazine*, Lent, 1960.

If illness is really God's will, then to try to cure it is an impious effort to defeat God. The work of Christ seems an answer to this.[2]

Is it not truer to say that God's will is *temporarily* defeated by illness just as it is by sin? Even though in illness the individual may not be at fault, his illness is *evil*, part of the world family's liabilities of ignorance, folly, or sin. It is something we ought to try to remove. As individuals we enjoy the human family's assets of knowledge, wisdom, and goodness. Similarly, because we are so closely bound to one another, we suffer as individuals from the family's liabilities.

The point that God is not *finally* defeated; that he can weave illness and indeed sin (e.g., the Cross) into his master plan, I will not now pursue. Clearly, God often uses a time of illness to deepen character, but that does not make illness his "will." It illustrates his way of bringing his good out of man's evil, but God does not need evil to accomplish his good. And it is not illness but *man's right reaction to illness* which brings the good. Any idea that suffering of itself brings holier character can be punctured by asking ourselves whether howling toothache of itself makes us feel noble, and then asking those who live with us whether they agree.

Beginning, then, with the fundamental thought that God wants all his children to be well and that we must all—including the patients—work to secure that end, the next fundamental idea, in my opinion, is that all healing is of God. With-

---

[2] I have worked out more fully the problem of suffering and the will of God in *The Will of God* (Nashville: Abingdon Press, 1954) and in *Prescription for Anxiety* (Nashville: Abingdon Press, 1956).

out the power of God, which is often called in this context "the healing power of Nature," the severed sides of a cut finger would never "heal." No man has ever healed another man. All he has done is to co-operate with God. Surgeons, doctors, nurses, physiotherapists, and others (not forgetting the dentists) co-operate with God on physical levels; psychiatrists, on mental levels; ministers and praying Christians, on spiritual levels. One of the most important matters to decide is the answer to the question: *"Which is the most relevant and helpful way of co-operating with God in regard to this particular patient?"* All healing is spiritual healing, for all healing is of God, and it is more relevant for a patient and *more religious* to have surgery than prayer, if, for example, the patient is suffering from an inflamed appendix, just as it is more relevant and *more religious* to throw water on a dangerous fire and summon the fire brigade than to kneel down and pray God to put it out. "Thou shalt love the Lord thy God . . . *with all thy mind."*

Our particular interest as Christians will be to co-operate with God on spiritual levels, and here we have a great opportunity and a wide field of service as long as we do not suppose that spiritual factors (e.g., prayer) will heal everything. Prayer has value in every situation, but not necessarily therapeutic value. If I have an abscess at the root of a tooth, I do not pray; I go to the dentist. I know what is the matter and who can put it right. If men develop cancer, they often ask for prayer for healing only because they do not know who can put it right. If they knew, they would not pray; they would go to him. Will God answer our prayer for healing if the power to heal is in our own grasp if only we use our resources; if, for instance, we, as a human family, would spend more on medical research and less on trying to reach the moon? Is our prayer for healing sometimes rather like a boy asking the teacher to do his homework for him? If God answered as we wish, he would end the agony of some by ending the resourcefulness of all.

This came home to me when I realized that in 1665 hundreds of good Christian people must have prayed that God would heal their dear ones of plague. But *if he had done so, and continued to do so, plague would still be with us.* Men would have put a prayer in the slot and drawn out a cure. They would never have resolutely tackled plague, found out why and how it attacked men, learned how to cure it and finally to prevent it. Cancer is now in that category, and the few must suffer that the family may learn. Finally, the few will feel it was worth it, and God has not deserted them or turned a deaf ear to their prayers. He has a concern for the private individual as Jesus so repeatedly said. Finally, all will be well for all, and no sufferer will feel that God has not justified his ways with men.

In the meantime, there is a vast area in which spiritual factors like prayer, forgiveness, spiritual insight, and love are healing forces. We are all familiar now with the so-called psychosomatic illnesses, those which show in the body but are caused in the mind or soul. It is said that more than one third of all sick people are brought low by nonphysical factors.

Guilt, exaggerated fear, hate, resentment, jealousy, inferiority, and so on, can all "touch off" illness and maintain for long periods illnesses first caused by physical factors. In this field lies the great challenge to, and opportunity of, the church, and I wish I could comfort some ministers I meet who do not think

20

they are doing much good in the world by saying that by faithful preaching—especially about love and forgiveness—they are doing a job of value in terms of preventive medicine. The worshiper on Sunday morning who accepts forgiveness may have saved himself months of a guilt-illness like some forms of skin trouble. She who puts resentment out of her heart during a church service on Sunday evening may have saved herself years of arthritis, as the sequel will show.

How are we to set about this healing ministry of the church? Let me start with negatives:

I am against services for healing to which, without preparation, all and sundry are admitted. My reasons are as follows. I put them down starkly here but have implemented them further in chapter 10 (The Case of Bert Abbott).

1. There is a terrible danger of the onus being put on the patient, so that if healed he thinks he has had faith when he may merely happen to be suggestible. Faith and suggestibility are far from being the same thing, but in "healing services" they are nearly always confused. It should always be remembered that we can have faith without being healed and we can be healed without having faith. If unhealed, the sufferer goes away with false deductions such as, "If I had had enough faith I could have been healed," or "God evidently has favorites," or "I am not good enough," or "Religion is no good." To encourage a sick person to believe that, provided he has faith, God must inevitably heal him, is unchristian and untrue.

2. The uninstructed try to "use" God as a means to their ends, as if physical health were the supreme end of man. This is false and dangerous. Better to be ill and humble than well and conceited!

3. The disappointment of the unhealed in the presence of the apparently healed not only can lead to false mental conclusions as in (1), but it can set up emotional depression violent enough to produce mental illness.

4. There is a real danger at healing services of mass hysteria strong enough to banish symptoms and lead a patient to believe he is permanently cured by God, or—worse—by the healer, only to be faced in a day or two with a return of the old symptoms or, more dangerously, new ones.

5. Resulting from (4) are two grave dangers: (a) the postponement of surgical help until it is too late, and (b) if in psychosomatic disease a symptom *only* is cured, even permanently, the unconscious, still unhealed, will set up a symptom *much harder to cure*. Hence our Lord's words, certainly not a threat, but a statement of what happens, "Sin no more, *lest a worse thing befall thee.*"

6. There is a lack of discrimination in the cases presented for healing. Jesus knew what was wrong with a patient, altered his treatment accordingly, and did not attempt certain cases at all. ("He healed *many* that were sick.")[3] The healer in some public services accepts all and sundry, does not know what is

---

[3] Two different Greek words are used in the Gospels, and there has been much discussion about them. One of them we should translate "to treat," not necessarily "to cure." The other only means "to cure." The sense of Christ's work among the sick seems to be that while he loved, cared for, and treated *all* who were sick, when it comes to *curing*, the sentence must stand "He cured *many* that were sick," but not all. I consulted a great New Testament scholar on this point. For myself I am convinced that Christ himself could not have cured every kind of disability. Could he have cured a blind man, both of whose eyes had been gouged out? Is the complicated structure of the eye rendered unnecessary at the touch of Christ? Could he have answered the prayer of a woman that she might have a child if her uterus had been removed? There must be countless situations in which prayer fails to bring healing because the apparatus is no longer functioning.

the matter, uses the same treatment for all, and puts the onus of recovery or failure on the patient. Heads the healer wins; tails the patient loses.

The positive measures which I would support enthusiastically are:

1. Intercessory groups of instructed people who will not lose heart at the admittedly very small percentage of sick people who are made well by prayer; intercessors who will realize that they can help change the way the sick person faces his illness, and that *this may be as important to his true well-being as recovery.*

2. Clinics made up of Christian psychiatrists, physicians, nurses, ministers, and deaconesses where "cases" can be discussed and the threefold energies of medicine, psychology, and religion focused on the patient. No "spiritual healing" movement can go forward, in my opinion, unless it be in harmony and close co-operation with the medical profession.

3. Ministerial private interviews giving to our Protestant people all that is of value in the Roman Catholic confessional and giving them insight into their difficulties, the light of God upon them, the mighty affirmations of our faith, and, where necessary, some simple technique of relaxation and suggestion.

4. Short, simple, healing services *by a patient's bedside or in his own room,* attended only by selected friends from the family and the real saints of the church, and including the laying on of hands and, if desired, the Holy Communion. This to be preceded by talks with the patient, so that if he is unhealed he makes no false deductions. If the "laying on of hands" is practiced, it should be made clear to the patient whether it is being done as a sacramental act signifying the forgiven patient's unity with God and God's blessing, or

whether it is a treatment involving "odic force" (see pp. 49-73).

When all this has been said, I want to add that we must be aware of the fact that healing sometimes takes place outside all techniques practiced as yet, and outside all our theories. Sick people get well. No one knows why. There must be a reason. The situation is rather like the opening of a safe by the correct use and sequence of certain numbers. Sometimes we hit by accident on the correct combination and the safe opens. In healing we must find out what the correct combination is. One of my secret hopes is that this book may stimulate inquiry into ways of healing into which so far we have only blundered by accident.

There are territories shouting for exploration, energies we have never tapped, laws—including those of prayer—that we do not understand. We must move ahead in this difficult field with diligence and devotion, in the spirit of reverent science and intelligent faith.

I

The Case of

MRS. COKER

Here is a remarkable case of healing in which I played a very unimportant, but a very interested, part. I shall present it mainly by means of the letters which Mrs. Coker wrote to me. She has given me full permission to tell her story.

At one time she had not much use for religion. Widowed, middle-aged, and arthritic, she seemed to have fallen into a rather dull and uninteresting phase in her life. The lines in her face were multiplying and her mouth was beginning to droop. After all, life isn't much fun for a woman in her fifties with rheumatoid arthritis and nothing to look forward to but the dull routine of an unpretentious home and the gradual extension of the disease.

One Sunday morning in June Mrs. Coker was in her kitchen preparing the Sunday dinner. Being rather bored as she cut up the vegetables, she turned the knob of her radio, expecting something very different from what she heard. Suddenly my voice over the radio said something that struck home to her heart, and on the same evening she sat down and wrote to me as follows: "You said something that made my life feel very ugly. . . . I don't suppose that I shall have the energy to post this letter even if I finish it, and in any case I am sure I shall

25

not have the energy to put things right and alter my way of living, and I don't quite know why I am writing at all."

Having received this letter, I wrote to a Methodist minister friend of mine who then lived in her neighborhood, and he was kind enough not only to call on her but to befriend her. In time, she found a real Christian experience and became a member of his church. Readers will imagine how thrilled I was at her conversion.

I was so happy and impressed at what had happened that at a subsequent service broadcast from the City Temple by the B.B.C. some years later, I told her story much as it has been given above. Once more, Mrs. Coker was listening in. She heard what she could not help but recognize as her own story, though, of course, I did not mention her name. That night she sat down and wrote to me again, and she has given me permission to quote from her second letter:

I listened to your broadcast last night. It is strange that, although I have often heard you speak in different programmes, I have never heard you on a Sunday since that unforgettable morning when I tuned in a few years ago. Strange, too, that I should hear your reference to myself. Yes, things have been put right, and I would like you to know that the woman who listened, and afterwards wrote to you, is a very different person today. I didn't know that God was speaking to me then, and I had no use for Him and no place in my life for Him. Today, He *is* my life. He turned my whole life upside down. There were many things, as you know, that had to be put right and many difficult decisions that had to be made. It seemed hard at the time, but today I am free from it all. My heart is too full of thanksgiving and praise for me to express in words. . . .

I can look back now over the past years and see quite plainly the way God has led me. As you know, I have been very crippled with arthritis and all sorts of odd complaints for over thirty years and before I left B—— I had rather a bad time. The doctors then told me that there was nothing that could be done, and that I should get worse, probably losing the use of my legs. I certainly did get worse, but last June there came an urge to walk without the help of my stick. The feeling that I must walk was so strong and definite that I knew I must, at least, make the effort. I walked and I was completely healed. From that moment I have never had any pain, and my legs have grown stronger every day, and now I can walk for miles and enjoy it. Last August I climbed to the top of Snowdon and down again. Oh! surely God has been good to me!

My heart is so full of thanksgiving and praise to God. I can't understand why He should have become so real to me, or why He should have been so good to me. I feel so awfully unworthy. Maybe this letter is unnecessary, but, please understand, it is only that I am so very thankful.

Of course, it would be quite wrong for sufferers from arthritis to suppose that their illness is necessarily in any way connected with their spiritual condition. Arthritis is "set off"—not caused—by many factors other than the one alluded to above, such as resentment, shock, hate, and worry. At the same time, this joyous story of immediate and complete recovery from disabling and long-standing illness offers a bit more evidence of a truth I have long attempted to get over to the public— namely this: If the mind-soul (I do not discriminate for the sake of the argument) is asked to bear a disharmony over a protracted period, it will sometimes, as it were, hand over its disharmony to the body, as though to say to the latter, "I cannot bear this any longer. You must bear it." Thereupon the body develops what appears to be a physical disease, and which, without doubt, is physical in its symptoms, but indubitably spiritual in its origin; that is to say, the physical illness is a translation into physical disharmony of what is fundamentally a spiritual disharmony.

Readers will ask why it should be arthritis and not something else. The choice of symptom on the part of the unconscious mind is too complicated for me to explain fully here. Briefly it may be said that the unconscious part of the mind chooses the symptom. No "malingering" comes into the matter at all, for we have no direct control by conscious means over the unconscious choice referred to. The following factors sometimes determine the unconscious in its choice of illness. We must remember that the mind must make the body convincingly ill so as to get itself (the mind) out of its distress.

1. If there is a hereditary or congenital weakness in the patient, clearly the unconscious finds it easier to seize on that. This determines sometimes why, after a general shock like an air raid, an earthquake, fire, or storm, one patient develops tuberculosis and another arthritis.

2. If the patient has observed that an illness gets another person out of a predicament, his unconscious will hit on the same disease for him. "No wonder I get asthma," said one of our clinic patients, "my mother has had it all her life. I've got it from her." Only then did the mother reveal for the first time that the patient was an adopted daughter, ruling out the possibility of heredity.

3. Sometimes the physical symptom has what could be called a "mimic" origin and determination. The patient goes through a contortion, or suffers a pain, which in some sense mimics the situation which caused his mental shock. Thus

one man, terrified by falling beams in a house bombed while he was in it, continually ducks his head even now, as though reacting the original traumatic situation. Another patient, whenever he becomes afraid through guilt and the fear of discovery, has a severe pain in the buttocks. In boyhood he was caught by a shopkeeper in the act of stealing, and the shopkeeper, entering behind him, gave him a severe "kick in the pants," the pain of which is reproduced even now that he is grown up. A medical student known to me had a severe pain in his arm whenever he needed love or approval or indulged in self-pity. As a child, a broken arm had brought him affection and consideration from parents who had not wanted him and who treated him coldly. It was as though his mind said to him, "When you were little, you got sympathy and love by having a painful arm. Now you need sympathy again, so try the same dodge!"

4. A symptom is sometimes determined by the fact that, so long as it is maintained by the unconscious, the patient cannot "lose face" or "give himself away." Thus a man who had a guilty secret and was terrified that he would drink too much and thus talk too much, or that he would talk in his sleep and give himself away, became dumb. So long as the unconscious maintained the dumbness—which it did for a long period—the patient was safe.

5. It should be remembered that, if a patient is likely to benefit by the continuance of a symptom, then one which in the beginning had a purely physical origin can be maintained for months or years. Thus one of our City Temple Clinic patients, traveling in Southern Ireland during the war, ate unwisely and upset a stomach unused, in those days, to such a rich diet. But the "tummy ache" persisted until it had got

him out of several appointments which he particularly wanted to miss! It is incredible to those who have not studied the odd workings of the mind that pork chops and cream trifles should make a man ill from July to November, and that he should only recover *after* the date of a particularly unpleasant engagement!

Clearly, however, when the spiritual disharmony ceases, the physical illness has no longer any reason for existing and it clears up with miraculous rapidity. A similar case is seen in the New Testament story of the paralytic boy let down through the roof. His paralysis was caused by his guilt—that is to say, a physical disablement was caused by a spiritual disharmony, and the words of forgiveness, coming with all the authority and power of our Lord himself, ended the physical illness at once. At last the patient could "walk away" from his sins, the guilt of which had previously crippled him. (See Mark 2:1-12.)[1]

No arthritic sufferer, I repeat, should deduce that of necessity his illness is spiritually caused, but the story of Mrs. Coker and others like her does provide a clue to an important branch of spiritual healing. No mere laying on of hands by an itinerant "healer" would magically cure such a person; but repentance, forgiveness, and unity with God are powerful therapeutic factors. The minister referred to above, who won Mrs. Coker to surrender her life to Christ, did far more than did my merely spoken word over the radio. The latter merely challenged her. Her healing demanded far more than the touch of someone's hands or the words of someone's voice, but there is no doubt whatever in my mind that the grace and power of the living

[1] I have commented fully on this and the other healing miracles of Jesus in *Psychology, Religion and Healing*, op. cit., pp. 29 ff.

Christ which converted her soul at the same time cured her body.

A further letter from Mrs. Coker gave me many of the particulars which I wanted to have filled in. She allows me to quote again:

One day when reading my Bible, I specially noticed Romans 8, v. 11: "If the Spirit of Him that raised up Jesus from the dead dwell in you, He that raised up Christ from the dead shall also quicken your mortal bodies by His spirit that dwelleth in you." I can't tell you exactly what my thoughts were, but it seemed to me that if the same Holy Spirit Who could raise Christ from the dead, was indeed in me, I could surely pray that He would do something for me. Maybe I've got it all wrong, but from that day I really began to pray for healing. I reasoned that He had already done a far greater work in me than physical healing. I remember so well telling God that I was getting older, but if He would only make me to walk like other people, I would do all that I possibly could to help other people to know of His love and goodness. I expect you will think this all sounds childish and silly, but I was desperately in earnest. Then, one afternoon, after a fortnight of unusually severe pain, I was sitting quietly here when I had a very great urge to go out. I knew I couldn't walk, so I tried to forget it, but the urge was so strong and it seemed as if I was being told to go out and walk to a certain hill on the outskirts of ——. Flagstaff Hill is a local beauty spot and I had often wished that I could go there, but it certainly was an impossibility. Really it is only about a mile from here, but I couldn't possibly have got so far. Anyway, the urge to walk was so strong that I just put my coat over my shoulders and took my stick and very painfully and slowly hobbled out. Before I could get to the gate a voice seemed to speak to me, and told me to take my stick back and to walk in the name of the Lord.

You can imagine how I felt. I just threw my stick down on the garden, and started to do what at the time I thought was a stupid thing to do. I slowly walked down the road, and as I walked I forgot everything except the fact that I was going to see Flagstaff Hill. I climbed over four stiles, and crossed three fields, and eventually came to the foot of the hill. I remember standing there for a moment, and looking up to the top and thinking that I would never be able to get up there. While I was looking, I began the walk up through the bracken, and finally I found myself on the top of the hill. Even then I didn't realise what had happened. I continued my walk for about a quarter of a mile over the top of the hill, then came to an old tree stump and sat down to enjoy the view. There wasn't a soul about. Only the rabbits scurrying around and the birds singing, and it was all so beautiful. Then (and I find it difficult to tell you this, but I think you may understand), I felt a great sense of peace and a sense of another Presence with me, and I suddenly realised that I was healed and that I could walk like other people. All pain had gone. I simply can't tell you how I felt. All I could do was to sob, "Oh God!" over and over again. I know, and am sure that Christ was there with me. It is an experience that I shall never, never forget. I couldn't speak or pray, only weep. Oh, I do hope you will understand! Even now, at times, I can hardly realise that I can walk easily and freely. I suppose I stayed there for about an hour and then started to come back. All this happened last June when we had a very hot spell of weather, and, of course, the grass was very slippery and I wondered how I was going to make the descent. I was so afraid of slipping because my ankles and knee joints were still stiff and swollen. I needn't have worried. As I began to come down the hill, still weeping, I seemed to feel the pressure of a hand on my shoulder, and as if someone were telling me the best places to put my feet, and I didn't make one false step. From that day my legs have grown stronger and I can honestly say that I have not had a moment's pain. As I told you, I climbed to the top of Snowdon and back last August and felt no ill effects. Do you wonder that I feel that I want to let everyone know what a great God we have? My healing was wonderful, but I do feel that my spiritual healing was more wonderful, and I can never thank Him enough for all that He has done for me. I had been more or less crippled for over thirty years, but during the last few years had got very much worse. At times I couldn't cross a room without great pain, and indeed, life was a burden. But now all that is changed. Isn't it wonderful how He changes things when He comes into our lives? I've only one regret. I do wish, with all my heart, that I had met Him earlier. May I say, God bless you, Dr. Weatherhead?"

What a thrilling story it is! I only wish that all the people I know who are suffering could find the same deliverance.

Here is another relevant and true story contained in a letter which I am allowed to reproduce in full:

Dear Dr. Weatherhead,

It is nearly seven years ago since my feet and hands became affected by rheumatoid arthritis. In about three months I was badly handicapped. Pain was acute and continuous, and walking, or hobbling, as it quickly became, was a very awkward business. The ordinary everyday things that my hands had to try to do were a burden, and many of them an impossibility.

I went through all the usual methods of trying to find a cure, and then some of the less usual—homeopathy radiesthesia—I delved into Christian Science, chiefly because I so envied the calm serene outlook of Christian Science friends of mine. But I met with little success, although the doctor who used homeopathic methods, and also radiesthesia did relieve most of the pain—but it was only a temporary relief.

Life was very dark, and although I had never accepted the fact that I should always be crippled, there is no doubt whatever that I was very despondent.

Then a friend told me of your work, and I began by reading *The Transforming Friendship*, followed by nearly everything you have written, including *Psychology, Religion and Healing*. The message for me was your "theory" (for that is what it was to me, then) that ill-will and resentment are poisonous things, and that they can be at least contributory causes of illness.

I was desperately longing to be free of pain and the limitations which arthritis brings, but even more so, for some quietening of the storms inside myself, and my belief in God was either too weak, or not of the right kind, to lift me out of this inner darkness—a *blackness* it was, sometimes.

And so I began to examine my thoughts—and tried to go back to the days before I had arthritis. I lay on my bed every afternoon (this was essential because of the pain in my feet when I had been around all the forenoon) and I found that I was full of resentment, and had been for years. The details do not matter, but they concerned my husband, his parents, and a neighbour.

It was a very difficult thing to put all of this out of my mind. There was such a lot of it, and my brain kept insisting that most of it was justified. (I haven't got rid of quite all of it even now, I must confess, and I don't think I shall ever be able to reach the stage when I can see everyone as perfect, as my Christian Scientist friends feel we ought to do.) At any rate, I tried—and by trying, I found that the empty space left, filled up again—but with a peace and calm in place of the intolerance and disquiet. This was so real that it amazed me. To begin with it didn't last long—I had to have another "dose" of being still—still with God—very soon. But it is lasting longer and longer, and now, perhaps when I'm washing dishes, or going shopping, I have only to say to myself, "Be still," and I know, straight away, a release of tension and a quiet serene confidence that I can cope with the challenges that life will throw down.

And my hands and feet are improving beyond my wildest hopes.

People whom I have known by sight only, stop me in the street to ask what is happening that I can now walk so well. These same people had seen me, for years, shuffling along—sometimes, when things were really bad, in bedroom slippers. My hands are deformed, but I can use them—in more and more ways as days go by. I may say here that the friend who suggested the possibility of my actually talking with you, told me to have this letter typed. True, it would make easier reading, but I want to show you what my hand will do—not as a gesture of pride, but in the hope that you will perhaps rejoice a little, too.

When I saw you, I tried, rather unsuccessfully, to express my gratitude to you. I knew then, that your "theory" was so much more than a theory, and I am even more certain now. During the past few weeks, my father-in-law and then my own father have died. Many demands have been made on me—physically, mentally and nervously. I have been very sad, and exceedingly tired, but the peace and serenity remain and I have been more than ever conscious of the completely and utterly unlimited power that there is —waiting, as it were, until we ask God for it.

Can you wonder how urgent a need I have to say "Thank you"? —"Thank you" to God—and "Thank you" to you for helping me to find Him. I am only on the very first step of the road—and I slip and stumble often—but I do know that it is the right road, and with the help of God, I shall try to follow it for the rest of my life.

You must have many letters of this kind, and I hope this one won't tax your patience too much, in the reading of it.

In deep and real gratitude,
Sincerely,

I have only two fears in publishing the above stories. The first is lest anyone become depressed and blame himself, thinking that his illness is necessarily due to some spiritual factor. I am sure that the two women who have written what you have just read above do not imply this at all. In their cases, a physical illness was the translation of spiritual disharmony, and when the disharmony ended the illness ended too. But, alas, illness is not as easy to understand as this might imply. Some physical illnesses are caused by purely physical factors. Some may be due to mental disharmonies in the deep unconscious mind, over which we have no direct control; and others again, like those referred to above, are translations into physical illness of a spiritual disharmony. There is a place in the world for the doctor, the surgeon, the nurse, the masseur, the physiotherapist, the psychologist, the dentist, and a host of workers fighting the evil we call disease. But it is worthwhile trying to make sure that our illnesses are not spiritually caused and to make our communion with God as full and free as we can, knowing that he is far more eager to be one with us and to heal us than we are to be one with him.

But what a thrill for ministers of religion to realize that at every church service, in prayer, sermon, and hymn, people are pleaded with to put away resentment, worry, hate, guilt, and other emotions inimical to health, and to substitute love, trust, forgiveness, and so on. The sermon which offers the love of God, if acted upon, may save the worshiper years of arthritis or some other disabling illness. The sermon which offers forgiveness can end a state of guilt which, if long continued, might have brought suffering of mind or body or both.

The second fear I have is lest anyone should think that I had anything to do with these cures. Humanly speaking, something I had said or written opened up new roads of inquiry, and luckily—I repeat, "humanly speaking"—the patients got the numbers in the correct sequence and the safe door opened. (See p. 24.) But thousands suffer from arthritis whose harmony with God is not in dispute, and thousands have done all they know in all directions—medical, psychological, and spiritual. Thousands have a splendid faith and yet thousands remain ill.

All we can do is to go on seeking in the spirit of Sir Ronald Ross—a deeply religious man—who sought the cure for malaria and set out his frustration thus:

> I pace and pace, and think and think, and take
> The fever'd hands, and note down all I see,
> That some dim distant light may haply break.
>
> The painful faces ask, "Can we not cure?"
> We answer, "No, not yet; we seek the laws."
> O God, reveal through all this thing obscure
> The unseen, small, but million murdering cause.

At last he found the answer and wrote again:

> This day relenting God
> Hath placed within my hand
> A wondrous thing; and God
> Be praised. At His command,
>
> Seeking His secret deeds,
> With tears and toiling breath,
> I find Thy cunning seeds,
> O million-murdering Death.
>
> I know this little thing
> A myriad men will save.
> O Death, where is thy sting?
> Thy victory, O Grave? [2]

[2] Quoted from *Philosophies* by permission of Sir John Murray.

Can we collect instances of cure, collate them, find what is common to them, discover what needs to be done, so that these sporadic cures are no longer of the order of "hit or miss," "try anything once," and so on, but are *within the known framework of understood law*, remembering that law runs as much in the psychical and spiritual parts of the universe as in the material and physical parts? Otherwise it would not be a *uni*-verse at all, but a *multi*-verse; a madhouse in which the power to understand, even slowly, would be impossible; in which chance, whim, and caprice ran riot; in which no steady laws reigned dependably; and in which nothing could be learned.

II

The Case of

PHYLLIS BARCLAY

IT IS A BAD THING TO HAVE TO DO ONE'S WORK UNDER CONDITIONS of rush. Even though one can, at best, keep a place of peace within oneself, outward rush is apt to penetrate. Decisions have to be made hurriedly, and who shall and who shall not be seen has to be decided without a full weighing up of every situation. Staying once in a distant town, I had had so many letters from complete strangers that, without secretarial help, it was impossible to answer them adequately, or even to see all who wanted to talk over their problems. In this way I almost missed seeing Phyllis. A secretary was loaned to me for one precious day, and we sat down together to cope with a formidable amount of accumulated mail. Mrs. Barclay's letter was carefully read, but I asked the secretary to reply that little could be done in a single interview, and my time was so booked up that I was sorry not to be able even to offer help.

Usually such a matter would inevitably pass from one's mind, but curiously enough I could not forget this letter. Mrs. Barclay wrote very fully to say that her daughter, Phyllis, was seventeen years of age, and in her earliest years had been a bonny and healthy child always requiring the biggest sizes in clothing. At one time she had even weighed 140 pounds, so that her father had made fun of her size and appearance, but now she was rapidly going down hill until Mrs. Barclay feared she might lose her daughter if something were not done. The doctors had examined her carefully, and nothing could be found wrong with her except that she would not eat. It was not just a matter of having no appetite, but of a curious reaction to all meals. She would sit at the table and pretend to eat, crumbling up her bread, for example, but sitting through the whole mealtime without taking any nourishment at all.

At first the parents had taken little notice, but, as they became more concerned, Phyllis would adopt more complicated procedures. She would conceal in her handkerchief the food she wanted them to think she had eaten, and then secretly throw it away, or she would come in late from school so that she could have her meal alone without being under the watchful eyes of her parents. Her weight began to go down alarmingly. Her rounded young figure shrank until it looked like that of an old woman. Her menstrual periods stopped altogether and she was listless and unhappy. Mrs. Barclay wondered whether any new approach could be made through psychology or religion, or both, and wondered whether I could help.

If the town had been one where a psychiatrist had been practicing or if one had been near at hand, I should have recommended that he or she be consulted, for any trained psychiatrist could have helped her. But it really looked as though Phyllis was going to die if someone did not do something about it. Finally, therefore, seeing on Mrs. Barclay's notepaper a telephone number, I rang and fixed a date and time when she could come with Phyllis for a preliminary chat.

Nothing could have been less promising than the first interview. Phyllis did not want to come. She did not believe I could do anything. She did not want to be bothered. I saw her alone, but she hung her head, would not even lift a sulky face to mine at all, and answered not a single question without pressure, and then only with a monosyllabic yes or no. I then interviewed Mrs. Barclay alone. She was ready and willing enough to talk about Phyllis, but she could throw no light on this strange and baffling situation. Her husband, she said, had told her to write. He was sick of Phyllis and her "carrying on." It transpired that on several occasions he had threatened that if she did not eat her supper, he would "take a stick to her." He had disciplined her up to the age of twelve, though he had never touched her sister. On two or three occasions, even up to the age of sixteen, I was told that he had actually resorted to corporal punishment. This was, of course, no use at all and merely built up her emotional response to her father into pure hatred. For a girl of that age, the shame and humiliation were more intolerable than the pain. The whole home was emotionally poisoned and life was unbearable for everybody in it. With Mrs. Barclay's help I got Phyllis on the scales. She weighed eighty-six pounds.

It was at this point that I heard first of the much younger daughter, Pamela. She was everything she ought to be. The sisters got on as well, as sisters usually do, and both parents "thought the world of" Pamela. She was a normal, healthy schoolgirl, fond of games and good at lessons. Everybody, I was assured, liked Pamela.

Suddenly it occurred to me to ask Mrs. Barclay a question. Had she ever had any difficulty over Pamela's food? Mrs. Barclay thought a moment, and then said, "Come to think of it, I did, but only when she was a baby. She soon got over it. She's all right now." It was a lucky question. I was eager to know more. Had Mrs. Barclay fed her herself? No, she would not take to the breast at all. Had she had difficulty in finding a suitable food? Yes, they had tried everything they knew. Then came the golden sentence from which everything followed logically and ended in Phyllis's complete recovery. Said Mrs. Barclay ingenuously, "We've all three spent hours and hours coaxing Pamela to take her food." "Including Phyllis?" I asked. "Oh, yes," said Mrs. Barclay. "When Pamela was a baby, Phyllis used to have her on her knees for hours at a time, loving her and petting her and coaxing her to take her food."

Of course, the obvious thing to do next was to try to win the the confidence of Phyllis. The next time she came to see me she came alone and seemed a bit brighter. Her weight was no better, nor was her appetite improved, but with the help of a bit of humor, we got nearer to each other. In a session of quiet relaxation and light hypnosis, I asked Phyllis what benefit she derived from starving herself. Her answer of three words was significant: "Revenge on father." Asked the same question a second time, she said, "Mum and Dad get worried about me." After she wakened I asked her another question. "Phyllis," I said, "would it be possible for you to continue your schooling if you stayed away from home for a bit?" At first she was shocked at the idea. It was impossible. Her parents would never allow it. Besides, she knew no one who would take her. Then came tears. "No one wants a nuisance like me," she sobbed. "I wish I could die." This was no mere hysterical symptom. It was getting dangerously near the truth.[1]

Luckily—was it luck, or was it all arranged in the unseen?—it was easy to fix up. Some ideal parents, with a little family of

---

[1] A case of a patient who died through anorexia nervosa is discussed in my book *Psychology and Life* (New York: The Abingdon Press, 1935).

their own, lived four or five miles away out of the town. Their house was literally at the seaside. You crossed a road from their front garden gate and you were on the beach. I had been able to do a trifling thing for them and they had said, with obvious sincerity, "If ever we can do anything for you, you've only to let us know." In half an hour it was all arranged on the phone. They would love to have Phyllis if her parents consented. She could have the little room over the hall to herself, and it looked onto the sea. She could catch a bus every morning that would take her into town in time for school. They would make her one of the family. Phyllis said, "Daddy would never agree." I said, "Leave Daddy to me." She did.

Mr. Barclay wasn't a bad kind of man. He was very worried about Phyllis and worry had led to irritation and then to exasperation. "Funny thing," he said, "Pamela's never given us a moment's trouble, and yet Phyllis has been difficult ever since Pam was born." How significant were those last five words!— "ever since Pam was born."

I talked a long time to Mr. Barclay. I think I made it clear to him that the trouble was he had never wanted Phyllis. He had wanted a boy; had "set his heart on a boy." That the eldest should be a son seemed to him the ideal, and it had become a fixed idea. Besides, a boy could have carried on his father's business and given him relief in his old age. So he had a "down" on Phyllis from the start. He had never said so, never told even his wife, never admitted the injustice of it to himself. But words cannot exaggerate the sensitiveness of the mind of a little child, especially where love is concerned. Here was a new and terrible illustration of the effects of the deprivation of love.[2] They might give Phyllis food and clothes and

---

[2] See *Psychology, Religion and Healing*, op. cit., pp. 343 ff.

education, treat her outwardly as they treated Pamela, whose femininity they didn't resent. But Phyllis's sensitive mind picked up as soon as it could pick up anything, that she, for some unknown reason, had educed disapproval from her parents, and particularly her father.

Of course, it was necessary for me to see Phyllis as often as I could. My questions were unpardonably pressing and intimate, save that her own health hung in the balance. When pressed and assured that she was not being disloyal to her family, she admitted some terrible facts. When *she* came home from school, her father did not even look up from the evening paper. There was no greeting, no friendly inquiry. When Pam came in it was so different. "Hello Pam! Have you had a good day? What have you got to do for your homework? Did you win at the hockey match?" But for Phyllis—silence, and unmistakable disapproval.

Phyllis was gradually persuaded how important it was for her when she came to see me, to give expression to all her emotions, the inward resentment of her spirit accumulated over the years. She quite quickly guessed the truth, "I ought to have been a boy to carry on the name in Daddy's business, but how could I help it?" She really despised her mother for being a cipher and being too afraid of her husband to win justice for her daughter. When mother and daughter were alone together it wasn't so bad, but Phyllis felt that no one really liked her or wanted her for her own sake. Pam treated her decently, but they couldn't be friends with such a disparity in the respective values affixed to them in the eyes of the parents.

Then gradually the changes I had longed for and planned for began to take place. Our interviews ceased to be orgies of tears, exploding passion, and abreacted feeling. We began to laugh together. For her, life was ahead—a full, joyous, self-giving life! Away with the melancholy of the home as it was! If things didn't alter, she need never go back to it. The future was hers. God was watching over her and wanting her happiness. His beautiful world was calling to her. Stars shone, flowers bloomed, waves danced, children laughed, and no doubt there were lovers ahead in the hidden years, but who would want to marry a skinny scarecrow who only weighed eighty-odd pounds!

Soon her weight was increasing every time I saw her. Her menstrual periods returned to normal. Finally came a discovery which she had to make herself. It was one I had guessed at long ago, as no doubt the reader has already. Here was a loving girl who wasn't loved. How could she win love? Love is the food of the soul. If it cannot get it, it will seek a substitute. If it cannot get even a poor substitute it will take to self-pity or cynicism or bitterness. Psychic drugs one could call them, but poisons too. But the mind will search and search first for some way of winning love. The conscious mind of Phyllis had given up the quest for love. Her father didn't want her, her mother was afraid of her father, her sister was content to bask in the approval given to her and did not notice how starved her sister was. At school Phyllis was happier than at home, but then it is home that matters. It is the love of our home folks that is the soul's first requirement. Fame and outside popularity and wealth and health and "all the blessings of this life" do not make up to the soul for the feeling of being unloved and unwanted at home.

But the *unconscious* mind of Phyllis had not given up. Far from the level of consciousness, like some devil in a dark and

45

haunted underground cave, whispered a voice telling her to starve. Let it be repeated that she was quite unconscious of all that was going on in the cave, save that she inwardly felt she must not eat. A patient in a like case to her own who actually died of this illness was quoted in the press as saying continually, "I feel there is some voice within me telling me not to eat." No words could put the matter more clearly. It was the unconscious mind making a life-or-death, do-or-die effort to win love. Phyllis, when I first met her, was far from following the argument, but it went thus: "You are not loved. You need love. Your sister gets love. She got a loving interest taken in her in early childhood *by refusing to eat.* Just at the stage when you, Phyllis, were denied love, she won it by refusing to eat. Try the same thing! Don't eat! You will win sympathy. They will coax you. They may love you. And if they see your weight go down, they will begin to care. In time you will be dangerously weak and ill, and then surely they *must* love you. If not, you might as well die. *Then* they will care. Here is a poor young girl sacrificed on the altar of self-immolation! The whole community will care then. And what a revenge you will have on your family for not giving you love."

The day came when, in an interview, Phyllis said, "I keep thinking of the time I had Pam on my knee trying to make her take her bottle." "Go on," I said, trying not to sound excited. Said Phyllis, "I think she liked the fussing and that's why she wouldn't have it at once." "Go on," I said. "I wish I was loved as much as Pam is," she said. From that point it was easy. It would have been very bad technique to explain earlier. Phyllis had to find out for herself the whole psychological mechanism that led up to self-starvation. To win love, an unconscious mind that was still infantile was trying the same trick that a baby sister had successfully used to win affection.

One morning the friends who had given her a home during the treatment were alarmed. Phyllis didn't come down for breakfast. They thought she had overslept. She wasn't in her room. They became alarmed. Where had she gone? They contemplated ringing up the police. Then there burst into the breakfast room on that sunny morning a tousled-haired girl, her eyes shining, her cheeks glowing, her whole being radiating joy. "I went for a swim and forgot the time," she said, and then added the words that finished the treatment. "I'm starving," she said, sitting down to bacon and eggs.

One further talk we had, and that about religion. There is no need to dwell on that, save to say that Christianity is essentially a religion of love. At its best, the church is a fellowship of loving people who can bring in a wounded spirit who is hungry for love and at least give her something to take the edge off her hunger. In every church there are some people who can mediate the love of God. It would be well if the minister formed them into a group, so that he could bring people like Phyllis into it. For often a hungry soul is put off, rather than attracted, by the kind of people met at church. They are often so ready to criticize and disapprove. Phyllis was lucky. The people with whom she had been staying were keen church folk of the broad-minded, tolerant, and loving type. What do denominational differences matter compared with that essential? After a few weeks' preparation, Phyllis became a Sunday-school teacher with six toddlers in her care. She loved them from the first, and that brought her their love in return. How slow the unloved are to realize that only by loving others can we win love for ourselves! She reveled in preparing sand trays and plasticine and pictures for them.

Then came a test. Her mother was taken ill and rushed off to the hospital. Her father demanded that Phyllis should come home. She came to me. What was she to do? Mr. Barclay saw my point when we talked together about it. He rescinded his *demand*. He apologized to his own daughter. He invited her, as she was leaving school soon anyway, to take a hand in running the home till "Mum" was well again. She blossomed under such circumstances. Suddenly she was not just wanted, but *needed*. Her father couldn't praise her enough. When my interviews with her ended her mother was still in the hospital. Phyllis was still putting on weight. She sent me recently a letter which is as full of fun and health as a letter from a girl in her teens should be. The burden of it is a question. May she write me again if she gets too fat?

III

The Case of

LAWRENCE LUKE

PART ONE. ODIC FORCE
A Rediscovered Healing Energy

THE CASE OF LAWRENCE LUKE, WHICH I WANT TO DESCRIBE fully in the next chapter, will not be comprehensible unless I can describe the healing energy which is involved in it and in some other cases which have come under my notice. This healing energy has been called odic force, or odyle, or radiesthetic energy. Lest it should be thought that I am romancing, I hasten to add that I have addressed in London a meeting of doctors called "The Medical Society for the Study of Radiesthesia." They have their headquarters near Harley Street, issue reports from time to time, and have regular lectures delivered which I have had the privilege of attending. Some of these doctors use this odic force in their treatments. One, in Harley Street, London, has become a friend of mine, and though his theories need further exposition and clarification, I have seen some of his amazing results with my own eyes and can give a personal testimony to their value. He has kindly read and approved this and the following chapter. I refer to him as Dr. X.

The term "odic force" is the one which I prefer and shall use here. It derives from Odin, or Odan, or Wotan, the god of

49

ancient Norse mythology, who was the Scandinavian counter-
part of Jupiter or Zeus and whose power allegedly permeated
everything in heaven and earth. One might call "odic force"
the all-pervading energy. It was discovered, or rediscovered, a
hundred years ago, though its discoverer was scorned, derided,
insulted, and then ignored. Now, in my opinion, inquiry into
it is leading us into a conception of a part of the universe as
epoch-making and wonderful as astronomy has made the starry
heavens, and nuclear physics atomic energy.

In Stuttgart, from 1788 to 1869, lived a brilliant chemist
called Karl Reichenbach, a contemporary of Michael Faraday.
His ability as a chemist was recognized by all. He was the discoverer of both creosote and paraffin (1830). He was not a
doctor of medicine, but of philosophy.

His researches into magnetism led him to a discovery which
perhaps he would never have made had he not had the help of
what is technically called a "sensitive"; i.e., a person with abnormal psychic powers, including clairvoyance. Reichenbach
found that "sensitives" could see apparent emanations from a
magnetized bar which they described as streams of light.
Reichenbach himself was not a "sensitive," but he discovered
that "sensitives" could also see such emanations from certain
metals, crystals, from matter which was undergoing chemical
change, and from the human body, much more marked with
some people, but discernible in all.

Reichenbach first thought that this power was a quality of
magnetism. He tried many experiments with it, and it was he
who first called it "odic force." He also thought it to be similar
to light, and in 1850 he published a four-volume work called
The Laws of Odic Light. But later he declared that, though it
was a real force which could be measured (e.g., he estimated

that it took thirty seconds to traverse one hundred feet of iron wire of a stated caliber), it differed from heat, electricity, magnetism, or light.

Reichenbach, in his ponderous treatise,[1] discovered many things which stretch the credulity of one who comes newly to the subject. He found, for instance, that the hand of a "sensitive" adhered to a magnet "as a piece of iron does," and that water which had been in contact with a strong magnet could be distinguished by a "sensitive" from ordinary water. A strong magnet caused the hand and arm of a cataleptic medium to move toward it as far as the body would allow.[2] He found, moreover, that water could be "odicized" by using the fingers of the hand, which, to the sensitive, produced the same results as a magnet. To grasp a sensitive, as we do when shaking hands, produced a disagreeable feeling, but to grasp both hands, right to left and left to right, produced a warm and comfortable sensation. Reichenbach writes, "When I gave my hands to Mr. Incledon, and above all when I crossed them, he felt an intolerable headache."[3]

Reichenbach holds that this power resides potently in the sun,[4] but permeates the earth and everything upon it. All things conduct it, but loosely woven, net-like materials hamper

[1] Researches on Magnetism, Electricity, Heat, Light, Crystallization and Chemical Attraction in Their Relations to the Vital Force, by Karl, Baron von Reichenbach, tr. by William Gregory, professor of chemistry in the University of Edinburgh (London: Taylor, Watson and Maberly, 1850).

[2] Op. cit., p. 25.

[3] Pp. 81-82, 176.

[4] P. 96. Reichenbach believes that the magnetism of the earth acts as a magnet in the laboratory and discharges odic force. He taught that if people would arrange their beds with the head to the north and the feet to the south, they would sleep better, as the lines of force would run with and not against the lines of force in the body. He taught, regarding the latter, that the right hand corresponds to the northward and the left hand to the southward.

51

its flow, and silk partly insulates it. Nylon, unknown to Reichenbach, appears to be impenetrable by odic force. Iron wire carries it successfully, and odic force was detected by a sensitive after it had passed along an iron wire thirty-three feet long and .0794 of an inch thick. The force was seen by the sensitive as "a slender column of flame, ten to thirteen-and-a-half inches long with a breadth of .8 of an inch." [5]

Odic force appears to increase in the body by taking food, by being in the sunshine, and by general physical fitness. Reichenbach writes, "Trials with Mademoiselle Maix and M. Schuh yielded the same results" (as those he had reached earlier). "They both found my hands more powerful after dinner than before it." [6] The light diffused by bodies possessing this force is exceedingly feeble and is not visible to every eye. Psychic sensitives see it. Other people, not psychically very sensitive, see it if they remain two hours in complete darkness. Then their eyes are frequently sufficiently prepared to perceive this light. During the two hours, the eye must not be reached by the smallest trace of any other light.[7] Even a sensitive, he adds, "cannot with certainty perceive magnetic light at a greater distance than forty inches." [8] Odic force resides in magnets, crystals, the hands, the sun, the moon, in artificial light, and in any matter undergoing chemical change, such as an acid or an alkali or an organic body undergoing decomposition.

Research into odic force is in its infancy. Very little is known, and I have a hunch that in the field of psychic re-

[5] Pp. 100-101.
[6] P. 196.
[7] P. 214.
[8] P. 355.

search and by investigation into the so-called aura that surrounds the human body, we may find clues which will help us to understand. Perhaps, indeed, psychic research will make us alter considerably the very primitive and elementary ideas we have about this form of energy. It is alleged by some writers that odic force can be most readily introduced into the body at the "chakrams," that is, the "power centers" of the etheric body which covers and to a short distance overlaps the physical body.[9]

It is said that one's right hand is negative and one's left positive; that a psychically sensitive person—unless left-handed—would prefer to have his left hand shaken rather than his right, for then negative flows to positive and is not repelled by its like. It is alleged that a sensitive can tell in which hand a person possessing odic force has held a glass of drinking water. Held in the right hand (the negative one) the water tastes pleasant; held in the left (the positive) it has an unpleasant taste. Conversely, if a glass of water is placed in the blue light of the spectrum, the water to a sensitive will thereafter taste cool, pleasant, and slightly acid. A glass of water in orange or yellow light will, to a sensitive, subsequently taste nauseating, bitter, and distasteful.

A definition of odic force is difficult. I can only offer that put forward by Reichenbach himself in one of his letters. He defines it as "a current of energy which emanates from certain organic and inorganic bodies, including human bodies, plants, magnets, crystals, and so on." He thought that it was con-

---

[9] These "power centers" are situated: (1) at the crown of the head; (2) over the pituitary gland (roughly between the eyebrows); (3) over the center of the throat; (4) over the apex of the heart (roughly below the nipple of the left breast); (5) over the solar plexus (roughly the navel area); (6) over the spleen (southeast of the navel); (7) over the base of the spine.

ducted through all bodies which are continuous in structure. He thought that it accounted for the phenomenon of table-turning and the "passes" made by the hands of the old-fashioned mesmerist.

He believed also that the curious behavior of a pendulum—let us say of a pellet of cork hung on a thin silken thread—was determined by odic force. If the right hand of a sensitive touches the point from which a pendulum is suspended, the latter will swing. In his letters, Reichenbach refers to an experiment which he says proves that the right hand of a sensitive glows in the dark with a blue flame, the left with a yellowish-red flame. It is alleged that putrefaction gives off odic light; and the queer phosphorescence which sensitives have claimed to see over some of the graves in cemeteries may find explanation here. When a long period has elapsed after death, no phosphorescent light is seen even by sensitives, for putrefaction has ceased. Many ancient ghost stories connected with cemeteries in which ghosts or weird lights have been observed may have their explanation in "odic light" seen by sensitives.

Odic force, Reichenbach tells us, is discharged through the fingers and to some extent through the breath (cf. Elijah healing the widow's son—I Kings 17:17-22). It is faster than heat in traveling, and slower than electricity. It is not, like the latter, conducted over the surface of a conductor, but permeates it wholly. It is retained for some time in matter charged by it, and it is retained longest in oil. It is interesting that oil "blessed" by being held in a bishop's hand was used in the healing services of the early church.

Science up to now has rejected the theory of odic force largely because science has not invented what we might call an "odometer" with which to measure it. It does not affect the thermometer, or any other instrument in general use. Yet now scientists are considering it again, and it may well be that at our very fingertips we have an energy of unpredictable value, but it seems psychically rather than physically determined and is hereditary and not necessarily in any way related to religion, though some "healers" have said it was the New Testament "gift of healing" with which Christ endowed the apostles. I have, however, seen it in use by those who deny religion.

I recently watched some interesting experiments on a purely scientific basis, and without reference to religion, performed by a medically qualified friend whom I will call Dr. X, in the neighborhood of Harley Street. He has, in a marked degree, this power which other "healers" have. It is capable of producing muscular movements or twitchings in some patients. Whatever it is, it is frequently felt as heat. Some time ago, Dr. X held his extended hands a few inches from the skin of my bare shoulders—I had had some fibrositis—and all day my shoulders burned as if they had been poulticed. The pain disappeared. A friend of mine, a bishop, had his fibrositis banished in a few moments by Dr. X in the same way. Other healers have told us that their hands communicate this kind of heat.

But the mystery deepens. It is well known that psychically sensitive people, called "dowsers" or "water diviners," can detect the unseen presence of water because their muscles twitch when they pass over it. They frequently hold in their hands a twig, but it is their muscles, not the twig, which are sensitive. The theory is that every substance sends out waves of a psychic kind, and the wavelength differs according to the substance that transmits it. The emanation of energy from the diviner meets the emanation from the water, and their

55

meeting sets up a muscle spasm. These wavelengths can be measured. Dr. X showed me his chart with the calculated wavelength set up by every element known to chemistry. He recently "discovered" a precious metal under a lonely moor by this method. His ideas were vindicated when engineers acted on his instructions and brought the metal to the surface.

Conditions of disease, it is alleged, throw out varying wavelengths according to the nature of the illness. The tubercle bacillus, for instance, or TB germ, sends out wavelengths at seven-inch intervals which have been measured and which a psychically sensitive person can "feel." I was shown a bottle of TB germs at one end of a brass ruler divided into inches, and then shown an instrument which at regular distances (representing the wavelength) "detected" the presence of TB. This instrument, placed near the lungs of a TB patient, gives the same indication at the same distances, and appears to confirm a TB diagnosis.

Where there is pain in the body, psychic energy is being lost, much as static electricity is "lost" by running to earth. At this "pain point," by holding his hands in a certain position almost touching the skin, Dr. X appears able to drive his own odic force into a body powerfully enough to send it up the nerve paths to the seat of the pain, often with what appears to be a miraculously therapeutic result. Dr. X believes it to be a perfectly normal form of energy not yet understood but rapidly coming under the survey and understanding of science.

The most remarkable thing I have seen in my visits to Dr. X's rooms was the case of a young woman with a twisted pelvis, who, when he placed his hands near, but not touching, her thighs, twisted her body in a most strange way. He said the body was trying to heal itself, to correct the faulty twist, in response to the force passing from his hands and meeting the discharge of psychic energy from her pain, much as a water diviner's hands twitch in response to the emanations from water. Others have called these movements "righting reflexes." I found to my amazement that I could induce this reaction on her also.

Remarkable to me—who am not consciously sensitive in the psychic sense—was the discovery that, when asked by Dr. X to tell him which part of a patient's back was causing her distress as she lay face downwards on his couch with her back exposed, I had only to run my hand down the length of the spinal column a few inches from the skin surface to feel unmistakably a sensation of pins and needles in my hand at one particular point, which turned out to be the focus point of the pain. Dr. X said that emanations from the pain spot met the odic force from my own hand and set up the sensation in the latter.

On another occasion, I took the late Bishop of Lichfield, Dr. Woods, to see Dr. X. At that time one of the latter's patients was a little girl of three who had been discharged from a famous children's hospital in London, her mother having been told that the child had been injured at birth and would never walk. I held my own hands with Dr. X in the appropriate places, one hand at the base of the spine and the other between her thighs. Our delight can be imagined when the child moved her legs for the first time in her life and said, "Mummy, I can move my legs." The mother was overcome with tears of joy, and indeed the Bishop and all of us were deeply moved. The child can now get into a crouching position and, with a good deal of help, can stand on her feet.[10] Dr. X is a deeply religious

[10] Since writing this account I have learned that the child can walk.

person, and believes that odic force is *increased* in its power to heal by prayer and meditation, though neither is essential to its possession.

It may be that here we have a clue to the understanding of the undoubted healing gift which some people possess, and I must say that investigation in the radiesthetic field seems to me more likely to bear fruit than investigation into spiritualism, where it is supposed that the so-called dead return and possess certain people and guide them to locate injury and treat the sufferer. I am not deriding the spiritualistic hypothesis, but to me it seems less likely.

The uncanny way in which some spiritualist healers find the correct spot where pain and disability and disease lurk, and do so often without being told by the patient or his friends where the pain is or what the diagnosis may be, is possibly due to the sensation set up in the hand by odic force in the manner described above.

Researchers have been working in this field for many years, but it must be said that only a beginning has been made. The difficulties are enormous, and the prejudice against unorthodoxy in healing methods—while it probably safeguards patients against cranks, charlatans, and fanatics and prevents treatment running too far ahead of theory and understanding —slows down the rate of progress.

Twenty years ago a specimen of blood from the finger of one of my children, sent on a bit of blotting paper to a "radiesthetist," led her, by holding a pendulum over it and over certain biochemic salts, to prescribe a remedy which entirely cured a most obstinate and longstanding disability which had made the child's life miserable for years.

Today, if a diagnosis is doubtful, one may send a spot of

blood to a laboratory in a famous city and receive not only a confirmation or otherwise of the diagnosis, one can *actually receive a photograph of the affected part* showing the damaged structures. Though the patient may have remained all the time in London, the blood spot emits radiations which disclose to the scientist working there the nature and scope of the disharmony. Each disease radiates its own characteristic wave form, and a method has been found whereby a "force-field" photograph can be taken of "the condition of any cell group in the body," the photograph showing not only the pathology but the state of the tissues involved. I have actually seen a photograph of the tuberculous lungs of a patient, showing clearly the extent of the disease, taken while the patient lay in a London hospital. *The instrument which took the "photograph" was fifty miles away.* All that was required on the spot was a drop of the patient's blood or a specimen of sputum. A friend of mine suffering from disseminated sclerosis sent up a blood spot and received a "photograph" of her own spine, showing white areas in the spinal column which, in the opinion of a consultant, *could* be the areas affected by the disease, but this patient received no benefit. I have also seen a "photograph" of a cow's stomach showing the presence in it of a length of wire and a large stone. *It was taken forty miles from the cow.* A veterinary surgeon confirmed the experiment by removing both wire and stone.

If, by now, the reader is about to lay this book down and declare that its author is mad and that the reader cannot be asked to believe such nonsense, I will only remind him that fifty years ago if someone had told him that, by watching a screen in his home, he could see and hear in London something that was happening *at that precise moment* in Edinburgh, let alone New York, he would have made a similar reply. We are moving forward to discover that there are energies at work in the universe more wonderful than we have dared to dream.

Recently I was called upon to give evidence in the High Court in what was popularly known as the "black box case." Much remains obscure, but I am glad that the defendants won their case and were exonerated by the trial judge from any stigma of deceit or charlatanism. They have "got something," and we can scarcely at this stage say more than that, but it may turn out to be something which modifies our whole outlook in dealing with the sick.

As long ago as November 28, 1954, the *Sunday Times* of London published the following:

Orthodox medicine now has its own "magic box" in which it can diagnose the ailment of a distant patient from a drop of blood on a sheet of blotting paper. The paper is inserted into the box with its ends in electrode baths and current is applied. Sixteen hours or so later, when the paper is removed, dried and dyed, it gives a coded picture in black or coloured bands of the patient's disease.

Addressing a meeting at the Royal Society of Medicine, Dr. F. V. Flynn of London University College Hospital's Department of Clinical Pathology, said that, in certain conditions, the picture obtained was "virtually diagnostic."

Though superficially the instrument may resemble certain notorious magic boxes denounced in the past by the medical profession as frauds, it works on a simple, authentic scientific principle. Everyone's blood serum contains a number of protein substances. When a drop of serum is placed on a sheet of absorbent paper and subjected to an electric current these proteins pick up a charge and start to move towards one or the other of the electrical poles.

They move at different rates, so that after several hours the units, which take up certain dyes, show up as bands on the paper. In health the proteins show a characteristic pattern; in disease the pattern is distorted.

Before we pass on to study an actual case of mine which illustrates "odic force," I would utter a caveat. Odic force is no "cure-all." It seems effective in some cases where inflammation is present or where rheumatoid trouble exists, but it fails to have any effect on many diseases, and where it will help one patient with, say, his arthritis, another's arthritis seems unaffected. Probably there is a psychical factor involved. The famous black box does not "work," I am told, unless a "sensitive" either manipulates it or is standing by it.

Again, odic force is often only temporary in its therapeutic value. Many "healers" owe their "cures" to it, cures often overpraised and exaggerated in the press, which is not interested in the subsequent return of symptoms. I saw a man treated for arthritis by Dr. X who was so thrilled by apparent immediate cure that he was ready to throw away his crutches. I was amazed to hear Dr. X say, "You will be just as bad tomorrow"—and he was. But repeated treatment over many months brought him, not cure, but immense relief. I have already referred in this book to dangerous "healing missions" and "healers" who advertise cures without waiting to see if the cure is permanent. I now dislike the phrase "faith healing" because its success is often only temporary, and not faith, but a certain kind of psychic makeup, is the factor involved.

Let me illustrate from an actual letter written to a friend

of mine who gives me permission to quote it from the paper in which it was published.

I wonder if you have ever had any experience of so-called Faith Healing. Last year I had a fall and injured my back and it has left my right leg lame and I walk with a limp. I have tried numerous remedies, but nothing does me good. At last, through a friend, I heard of a healer who was holding services here in London and I was fortunate (I thought) in getting a ticket. So I went last Thursday for treatment. The healer gripped my leg and I felt as if a galvanic battery was passing up and down it. When I came out I had a short walk to my bus and I could walk all right and did not limp. Naturally I was delighted and was thankful to God for healing me after much prayer. But to my amazement and disappointment the next morning my lameness was back and I was as bad as ever. I am quite convinced it could not have been Divine power or it would have lasted and I have come to the conclusion it is some sort of mesmerism he practices. Do you happen to know anyone who has had a similar experience and what is your opinion of it?

Well, I know hundreds who have had the same kind of devastating experience. It was not mesmerism. All that happened was that the patient had one quite insufficient treatment of odic force and then relapsed. His "faith" has had so little to do with it, and complete healing is so rare, that to talk of "faith healing" and put the onus on the patient to "have faith" is cruel and stupid. Poor patient, he pathetically and erroneously believes that if only he had had "faith in Christ" he would have been well.

On the other hand, when I visited Glasgow some time ago I was much impressed by the work being done by a body of ministers there who are engaged in healing through a Christian

62

group. I listened there one Sunday night to a healing service which one of them conducted over the radio. It was a service of immense power and beauty and could not fail to help—and, I should think, to heal—many a sufferer.

I was told a very extraordinary thing. One of the number of this Glasgow group was rung up on the telephone by a distracted woman who said that her little girl was dying of pneumonia. The minister, over the telephone, gave her an instruction which, had he studied odic force, could not have been more relevant. He told her to place one hand over the child's lungs and the other on the child's head and to keep them in that position for an hour, praying trustfully and positively and believing at the same time in recovery. The minister then rang up each of the other members of the praying group, and asked them to pray for the child in positive and affirmative ways which they had so often discussed together in fellowship. After the hour, the mother, as instructed, rang up the minister to say that the child already seemed to have improved and was sleeping peacefully. The child completely recovered.

In my opinion, the gift which Mr. Harry Edwards possesses is that of "odic force." He believes that he is controlled by the spirits of Lister and Pasteur and that they work through him. It is not for me to deny this claim. For myself, however, I feel that the "odic force" explanation of his gifts fits more easily.

In 1952 he was good enough to visit my home in London, where I had ten or a dozen patients whom I had been quite unable to help ready and eager to meet him. Alas, not one of them received the slightest benefit from his ministrations.

At his invitation, I went with the late Dr. Sangster to his center near Guildford and watched closely, sitting next to him, while he treated fifteen patients during one afternoon and early evening. While my impressions were fresh I wrote out a careful report on what I had seen and got Dr. Sangster to check it lest I had made any thing up or exaggerated. No one could help being deeply impressed by Mr. Edwards himself and by his amazing work. He is sincere, modest, and compassionate. There were some instances in which, frankly, he seemed unable to accomplish anything. One blind woman received no benefit. But under my eyes, a man who had had to be helped into the room and who used two sticks, limping painfully with arthritis, walked out without them and without pain; a woman's deafness appeared to be instantaneously cured; another woman of fifty, with arthritis in hip and spine, told us she had had an accident in childhood and had never walked since without a stick. Edwards, not by manipulation, but by passing his hands lightly over her knees, loosened them in a way which made her exclaim, "I have not done that for years." Soon she walked without any aids and with a new freedom. A man with sinus and nasal trouble, who said he had not breathed through his nose for years, went out with mouth shut, inhaling heartily through both nostrils. And so the story goes on.

What is needed, I repeat, is thorough scientific investigation and much greater understanding of the underlying laws which govern this strange energy. Then using it to heal will not involve the "hit-or-miss" situation of today or leave many patients facing the bewilderment of relapse.

Just in case any one should dismiss all this as "modern nonsense" I should like to quote what, according to Tacitus, Hippocrates, the father of medicine, once said:

It hath oft appeared, while I have been soothing my patient, as if there were some strange property in my hands to pull and draw away from the afflicted parts aches and diverse impurities, by laying my hand upon the place, and by extending my fingers towards it. It is thus known to the learned that health may be impressed on the sick by certain movements and by contact, just as some diseases may be communicated from one to another.

Hippocrates was born about 470 B.C.!

IV

The Case of

LAWRENCE LUKE [1]

Part Two

HE WAS TWENTY-SIX YEARS OLD WHEN HE CAME TO SEE ME twenty years ago, hobbling painfully with a stick and throwing his legs out from the hips with a most awkward gait. No one seemed to know what was the matter with him. He was the only surviving child, his sister having died of intestinal obstruction after only three weeks of life. The mother was thirty-nine when Lawrence was born. He was delicate, but had no unusual illnesses. At the age of five, he fell down some stone steps and hurt the back of his head. At eleven years of age his mother had remarked that he was knock-kneed. He found it painful to walk on his heels. At sixteen he had had an operation on the tendons behind both his ankles. After a further operation at an orthopedic hospital, he had spent three months in a cast from toes to knees. Still the walking did not improve. Special shoes were made for him. He slept with steel soles

---

[1] This chapter has been read by the patient and approved as a true account of the details of the illness in a letter dated January 25, 1954. The patient now (1962) walks without a stick and drives a car daily through London traffic on his way to business.

strapped to his toes. He had come to me to see if the trouble might, after all, be psychogenic and whether he could get help from our psychological clinic. The orthopedic surgeon had said, "There is nothing more that I can do."

Clearly the first thing was a further careful physical examination, and he was turned over to one of the doctors helping me. Gradually we assembled the reports. Lumbar puncture proved the spinal fluid negative. The Wasserman reaction for congenital syphilis was negative. The X-ray report reads:

Chest   Apart from some fibrosis and pleural thickening at the left base there is nil of significance.

Spine   Nil of significance.

The next step was to admit the patient to a hospital for nervous diseases for observation and inquiry. The diagnosis was Friedreich's ataxia. This diagnosis was confirmed by a Harley Street neurologist. It seemed that there was little more to be done. The patient, however, is a person of unusual courage and optimism. In his heart he rejected the suggestion of hopelessness and despair. One doctor—not one of my team—foolishly told Lawrence that quite soon—within six months in fact—he would be confined to bed and would never get up again. This gloomy outlook might have done grievous harm to a certain type of patient. Lawrence grinned as if to say, "I'll show them!" Lawrence was unfortunate in some of his doctors, for another said to him, "My sister died of Friedreich's ataxia. There is no cure!" Still Lawrence kept up his courage and a superb Christian faith on which he continually relied, joyously to find that it supported him in those inevitable dark hours, about which everyone who has ever been ill knows only too well.

The next step seemed to be a thorough psychological inquiry. Willingly the patient went to a famous psychiatric hospital in London and submitted to all kinds of tests, but here again all that he learned was that progressive deterioration of his condition was to be expected.

There was no neurotic condition that I could hit on, no likelihood that the lameness and the pain in the back were psychological in origin, and one did begin to feel beaten. We had tried everything and exhausted, as we thought, every possibility in diagnosis and treatment. Was all we could do to accept the diagnosis of Friedreich's ataxia and let this brave patient sink into invalidism, or at best struggle on without further help?

Then I tried hypnotism. The patient turned out to be a splendid subject for this treatment. Rapidly he dropped into a deep level of hypnotic sleep. Hypnoanalysis and persistent questioning while in the trance state failed to reveal any hidden psychological cause of his physical troubles, but suggestions of confidence, of a growing power to control his limbs, and of the power of God sweeping through his body seemed so to tone him up and enhearten him that I continued this treatment once a week. When this proved too demanding on my time, I taught his wife how to hypnotize him and make similar suggestions. This she did, and I saw him once a month only, and sometimes at much longer intervals, one of them of over six months, for I had undertaken a tour around the world. He had osteopathic treatment regularly and careful treatment from a chiropodist, but all of us together were only keeping him on his feet and helping him maintain his morale.

One day toward the end of 1953 he was in my study preparing to lie on the couch for a usual hypnotic treatment when he complained of a sharp pain between his shoulder blades. He had told his doctor about this and had been informed that he had been sitting in a draft. Treatment was given but Lawrence wrote (December 8, 1953): "Instead of it being painful only when I sit in one position for a long time, it now aches all the time." As he sat upright on my couch, I happened to pass my hand down his back without touching it, and was amazed to note a sudden convulsive movement which he insisted he could not help making. He removed his shirt and we continued this treatment of his back. Not only did he continue the convulsive movements, but he said that his shoulders burned with a most comforting glow and the pain entirely disappeared. When he lay relaxed on the couch, I found that wherever my hand was stretched out a few inches from his body, that part of the body tended to make a spasmodic movement and to feel a glow of heat, though my hands were not warm, nor was the suggestion of heat made to him. Thus we got ankles, knees, hips, wrists, elbows, and shoulders all flexible; and even the spine made a convulsive jerk as though the body were being manipulated by a ghostly osteopath! As the patient went down the stairs, he said, "You haven't by any chance slipped a hot-water bottle inside my shirt, have you?" I had explained to him something of the mysterious energy described in the last chapter and he wrote later, "When you can reasonably fit it in, can I ask for another dose of odic force? I am sorry if I appear to be demanding in this respect but really life is so very much easier and so much less of a struggle that I want to seize every opportunity I can."

Later still he wrote (January 25, 1954): "On Wednesday

I felt on top of the world after nine hours unbroken sleep on Tuesday night. All the aches have gone."

Is it the fact that in any condition of disease, the unseen aura which permeates the body and overlaps it carries in it a corresponding disease condition? Could the odic force from my hands radiate the astral body with healthful energies which are carried across this "etheric bridge" to the physical body, there to bring healing and power? And is this a clue which helps us to understand the healing which undoubtedly followed frequently "the laying on of hands" and the ministrations of psychic healers? These are questions which open up vast fields of inquiry, and I have no slick answers to give.

However, since that discovery with Lawrence I have seen him thirty times, giving him the same kind of treatment, first in the conscious state, and then, together with suggestions of muscular strength and control, in the hypnotic trance. The results have delighted us both. Under hypnosis the power seems even stronger. The word "cure" is not one to use too readily in any case. In this case it cannot yet be used. And if, as we hope, it *is* relevant, it could be asserted that the patient has never had Friedreich's ataxia, but something else. Indeed, the patient himself, who has come to understand a great deal about his case, has declared all along that the diagnosis was wrong. When he can play tennis again, I shall not mind what caused his lameness for so many years! We kept the treatment a secret between us, save that his wife and mine knew what was going on. But soon comments began to be made. The osteopath commented on greater flexibility of muscles and joints. The chiropodist noted a significant change of stance, and a fortnight later prescribed a different kind of pad for a foot which was flatter. Lawrence writes, "When my chiropodist massaged my legs and ankles this evening, she was amazed at the extra freedom of movement there was since a fortnight ago. She was the more amazed because the improvement was so swift, taking into account the fact that it is over twenty years since these muscles worked correctly." A cousin who had not seen him for a year commented on a new ease in walking. Then the osteopath noted that the hips and pelvic girdle were "level." An office colleague congratulated the patient on his walking. He never uses a stick now.

The patient, who formerly tired in half an hour of standing, recently went Christmas shopping with his wife—enough to tire an athlete—without noticing fatigue more than she did herself. Later he went for a holiday abroad and wrote:

Never in my wildest dreams did I imagine that my feet would stand all that was planned to be done, but, miracle of miracles, they did. I was able to do all that the other people did and still have energy left for more. I wasn't aware of my feet once during the whole holiday. It is impossible to describe the wonderful sense of relief to have been completely care-free. It is truly a miracle. . . . After all these years of slow progress, it is almost incredible actually to see these improvements so quickly.

I called Lawrence my guinea pig because he was the first person I ever tried to help by means of the "odic force" in my fingers. He wrote: "The guinea-pig is very grateful but I must admit that I find odic force most uncanny. All these miraculous things happen and you don't actually come into contact with the body."

I strongly disapprove of people who rush into print about miraculous cures, and the patient "Lawrence" still has a long way to go before such a word as "cure" can be used, but I

71

feel that here is a field for inquiry, investigation, and experiment. In the case of another friend suffering from a painful suppurating finger which would have had to be lanced, it seemed as if the repeated passing of my fingers near the site of the inflamation "drew the pain out," to use her own phrase. The finger was normal next morning. A similar thing happened with yet another friend who was subject to repeated boils in the nostril. A very painful one arose and the patient expected the usual unpleasant process of a treatment calculated to make it burst and the inflammation gradually to subside. Odic force, applied without touching the nose, brought about the complete disappearance of both pain and inflamation in one night. If it were suggestion only, all I can say is that I made no verbal suggestion and I have never seen so speedy a result in a long acquaintance with treatment by suggestion. Since this chapter was written, many patients have found benefit, but in some cases not the slightest improvement has been brought about.

Careful experiments under test conditions must be carried out. It may be that odic force is a power possessed in some measure by everybody. It may have been overlaid through the years because we have become so much more dependent on energies which we understood better. It may be that people who are psychically "sensitive" possess this power unknown to themselves. It may be that prayer increases it. Some of my friends feel quite sure that it does. It may be that its value depends on a psychic quality in the patient as well as the phenomenon of odic force possessed by the healer. It is the opposite of the true scientific spirit to deride it, to call it fanciful, to attempt to laugh it away. Let us find out the truth. That is all I am suggesting. For myself I believe—because I have seen the evidence with my own eyes—that at our very fingertips there may be a healing energy which, *in certain cases* of pain and disability, we could use to help our fellow men. The next chapter gives another example of the use of the same power. One begins to wonder whether what was called "the King's touch" may find a belated explanation here, and whether the practice in the early church of the "laying on of hands" may have not only sacramental value but actual therapeutic value through odic force in the hands of the ministrant. Since oil is known to retain odic force for a time, the anointing with oil, after the latter had been "blessed" by the hands of a bishop, may have had actual therapeutic value.

V

The Case of

CHRISTINE DOWER

THE CASE I AM ABOUT TO DESCRIBE IS A STRIKING TESTIMONY to the possibilities of odic force, and it is pleasant to write about a little patient who owes much to others, but nothing to me. I know her parents and I have checked the facts carefully, but I have never treated the patient myself. I have the parents' permission to tell you the following story, which they have read and approved as correct.

Christine's father is a young and capable Methodist minister who married a fine girl, who, with her sister, was a member of my "Friday Fellowship" at Brunswick Methodist Church, Leeds, more than twenty-five years ago. Responding to what they believed to be a call of God to do missionary work, this happy and devoted pair went off to Africa and Christine was born there in 1946. When I first began to write down her story, Christine was living with her parents in England. She was then eight years of age (January, 1954).

Christine, like most children in the tropics, had half a grain of quinine daily from her fourth week until she was ten-and-a-half-months old, when she came to England. She was a normal, healthy child and had begun to use baby talk. At fourteen months she was immunized against diphtheria. At this

74

time she began to hold her ears and sometimes lost her balance, "falling about the house," to use her mother's description. The parents, of course, noticed this, but thought it might be due to the immunization and they did not report it to the doctor. Mrs. Dower is allergic to most drugs, and it was surmised that Christine might be similar. Indeed, she does react violently to all barbiturates, as does her mother.

About this time Mr. Dower noticed that Christine looked puzzled and worried as she watched him using a typewriter. It then became apparent that she was deaf and could not hear it. Elementary tests at home speedily confirmed this.

A famous Leeds otologist (ear specialist) was speedily consulted. At first the specialist said that Christine was totally deaf and must have been born deaf. When the parents assured him that this was not so and pointed to the fact that Christine had already begun to use baby talk, the specialist then said she must have gone deaf through taking quinine in the tropics. He did not think the diphtheria immunization could be blamed, and he asked permission to write about the case in the British Medical Journal. Blood tests were taken of Christine and her parents, but no abnormality was discovered. Christine's skull was x-rayed, but nothing significant was discovered there either. It was stated by the specialist that the middle ear and eardrums were normal.

It was at this point that the parents turned to me. They lived a long way from London and could not at that point make the journey, so that I could only promise that in our intercession circles—of which we had six at the City Temple —we would pray for Christine and that at the next Sunday evening service the whole congregation—well over a thousand people—would concentrate in prayer for her. Temporary improvement followed immediately. "The following Wednesday"—I quote from the mother's own letter to me—"Christine could hear quite well, normally, so far as could be judged in so young a child." But alas, "a fortnight later the deafness returned."

By this time Christine was two years of age and the next step was to take her to the Department for the Education of the Deaf at Manchester University. Here she was carefully tested, and I print the report.

Christine Dower "came to our clinic on June 8th 1948.

Response to tests:

Percussion toys	Drum	ff at 3 feet.
	Bell	ff at 2 feet.
	Noisemaker	at 6 feet.
Pitch Pipes	120	ff at 6 inches.
	320	ff at 2 feet.
	1500	ff at 6 inches.
Voice	Very loud at 1 foot.	

"These results led us to the opinion that Christine is severely deaf, though she has residual capacity to hear the whole speech range, and we should expect her residual hearing would enable her later to benefit from training in the use of a hearing aid.

"We have advised Mrs. Dower to begin training her in lipreading at home and to continue under our guidance for twelve months."

Mrs. Dower tells me that at the insistence of a grandparent, Christine was then taken to see another otologist at ——, who declared that she was totally deaf and said that, in his opinion, it was due to having taken quinine.

At the age of three and a quarter, Christine began to attend

76

a school for the deaf in —— where her parents lived. She learned to lip-read very well and could speak whole sentences spontaneously, though her speech was far from perfect. A curious thing was noticed. The hearing fluctuated and seemed better when the child was unwell, say with a cold or sore throat. It was noticed that if Christine "ran a temperature" her hearing seemed improved. In a period of, say, three or four months, Christine would have one good day and then relapse into severe deafness.

Having kept in close touch with the case and having a personal friend in Harley Street with the F.R.C.S. qualification, who specializes in ears, noses, and throats, I suggested that Christine be brought to London and be thoroughly examined by him. This was done on May 19, 1953.

A letter to me from the specialist, dated May 21, 1953, says, "She suffers from bilateral nerve deafness of a very profound degree, although she has some hearing left in both ears; but she can understand only the very loudest shout when she is not lip-reading. Although she can make herself understood to a certain degree, her speech must still be regarded as very defective." The specialist then advocated that tonsils and adenoids should be removed and that Christine continue at the special school "where she will eventually, we hope, learn to speak more perfectly, so that in later years she will be able to earn her livelihood in any profession within the limits of her disability." I have a note that over the telephone the specialist said that it was hard to say what caused the deafness, but that *nothing medically or surgically could be done.*

The tonsils and adenoids were removed, but without any noticeable improvement, and things seemed to have reached an impasse, save that intercession for Christine was maintained.

At this point I must explain another matter. I am sure that many people, unknown to themselves, possess this odic force which I have described earlier, and could render great help to sufferers in certain kinds of case. Knowing that a minister, whom I will call Conner, had this power in a marked degree and lived much nearer to the Dowers than I did, I suggested to the latter that they should get in touch with Conner and ask him to treat Christine. Here is a letter from Mr. Dower reporting what happened, and dated September 15, 1953:

My wife took Christine to ——— (naming a city) on the 24th August and stayed until the 28th August, during which time Mr. Conner gave her eight treatments—"ear-warming" we've called it, for that has been the visible sign of something happening. Mr. Conner put his hands around, but not on, Christine's ears, and after some ten minutes or so, the ears went pink and later a deep red.

Christine said that first her ears were warm, then hot and then boiling.

Christine's hearing definitely improved with this treatment, and she even heard a telephone bell ringing in a bus depot across a road. We have reported to various doctors who have seen Christine that her hearing appeared to be better if she was running a temperature with a bad cold or similar ailment; there seems to be some connection between the increased temperature produced by the "ear-warming" and the improvement in hearing.

During the treatment Mr. Conner became convinced that my wife also possessed this odic force quite strongly and suggested that she keep up the treatment with Christine. From what I have seen it is quite certain that she has this power, for the same redness and heat are produced and Christine *continues to hear better than she has done for years*. (I almost wanted to put that last sentence in capitals!) On Sunday, 6th September, she heard me speaking to her on the telephone; on Tuesday, 8th September, she volunteered the information that she could hear a motor-cycle in High Street, and when I said "good-bye" to her last Thursday in a fairly loud voice, she covered her ears and said the noise was "awful"!!

It is difficult to say just how much better her hearing is for she just doesn't like sound now, especially when a number of sounds are jumbled together, and I do not think the improvement is yet sufficient to be useful to her. Her ability to hear still fluctuates, but the periods of better hearing come now every few hours instead of at intervals of several months as we had noticed before.

And now for another development. My wife tried out this "force" experimentally on a retired Wesley Deaconess who was injured in an air raid in 1940 and who has been very lame since and has been told by doctors that nothing more can be done for her. During the first treatment she reported a feeling of heat and tingling sensation, and could move her ankle which had been "locked" for years, and could move her knee better also. The friend, with whom this Deaconess lives, says that before seeing her, she could "hear" that she was walking differently! After the second treatment the Deaconess reported that the leg, instead of feeling like a trunk of a tree she was carrying around, now felt "alive" for the first time for nearly thirteen years.

What this is all going to mean we do not know. We do remember (who could forget?) your cautionary words about working with the co-operation of the medical profession whenever possible. My wife is somewhat apprehensive; she says "scared to death" which is an exaggeration, for she knows God will guide her in using this unusual power.

Mrs. Dower has continued this ministry with amazing success. Dozens of people have been healed by her use of "odic force," but that is another story. I think this record gains all the more because all along the parents have kept in step—as it were—with the medical profession, and they have never mentioned the word "miracle" or exaggerated the benefit which undoubtedly Christine has received.

It should be remembered that from the first Christine had had short periods when she could hear very loud noises, but they were at intervals of months. Now they are almost daily occurrences. On October 14, 1953, her father wrote:

She still has no useful hearing, maybe because sound is on the whole meaningless to her. We can tell in several ways how many more things she can hear, but she cannot yet hear normal speech. If I speak very loudly to her from a distance of six or eight feet, she now covers her ears and says the sound is "awful." Two months ago she would not have heard my speaking to her unless I had spoken a few inches from her ears. We want you to understand that in between these periods of hearing she remains, to all intents and purposes, completely deaf. My wife is continuing to give Christine this treatment. It is fascinating to watch. Her ears turn first red, and then deep crimson, and she says they are hot and then "boiling inside"!

A letter on October 28, 1953, says that "the improvement we noticed since she began treatment with 'radiesthesia' has been fully maintained." In January, 1954, Mrs. Dower wrote me:

She now hears many more sounds than she could and shows an interest in the wireless, turning it up very loud, and obviously she gets something from music. She also plays on the piano, but maybe what she gets here is a sense of rhythm from the vibrations. She still cannot hear normal speech, but can hear very loud speech at five or six feet. She now has an occasional bad day when she seems to hear nothing, but this is just the reverse of the position before treatment by odic force began, when Christine had only an odd day of hearing in the midst of two or three, or even four months of very severe deafness.

On February 23, 1954, Mrs. Dower wrote:

We have been away for a few days, during which time Christine has heard (and what is much more significant) appreciated a number of sounds which previously either she did not hear at all or was unable to recognise. Coming home last night, she said (as near as possible—verbatim): "Please write and tell Mr. Conner and Dr. Weatherhead that I can now hear motor-horns as well as cars and buses and a lot of things. I want Mother to warm my ears a lot more and then I can hear a lot more." The great thing is, that for the first time, she really desires to hear—hitherto, sound has been a meaningless noise and a nuisance to her. We took her to a panto-mime last week and she heard the orchestra and a shot off-stage and was able to identify both at once.

On another occasion, she offered the information that the man on the wireless had stopped talking—it was now music—and when questioned, she gave a fair imitation of a woman's voice moaning and said, "A woman singing."

Mrs. Dower herself has been able to bring comparative hearing to one person, comparative sight to another. Through her treatment a circulatory disease was cured in one case, and in another locked joints were released. A boy who could not use his right arm was enabled to carry two chairs with it. A woman of thirty-seven, diabetic since the age of five-and-a-half, was clear of sugar for seven consecutive days, and has now had

81

her insulin reduced to almost nothing. A man of fifty-six with arthritis was made able to do three hours' clerical work at a stretch, and the swollen knuckles became normal. Mrs. O, a blind woman on the totally blind register, has been to see her specialist in order to be removed from the register as she can now read the smallest print without spectacles. So read the reports which Mrs. Dower sent me of her own work (dated November 7, 1954).[1] We are but at the beginning of discovery in a field that may yield rich treasures, not only in actual treatments, but in our understanding of some of the mysterious but factual cures which through the ages healers have effected, sometimes in reference to religion, but often without any reference to religion at all.[2]

I can now add later details of this fascinating case. Here is a letter dated July 4, 1957, from Christine's father:

Dear Dr. Weatherhead,

We haven't written for a long while though often we have wanted to share some special joy with you.

You will be pleased to know that Christine's hearing continues to improve. The aural teacher at her school showed —— [Mrs. Dower] some graphs a few weeks ago charting the improvement. With a new transistor aid she can now hear *practically every sound*. She is recognising some speech now but it is going to be a super-

[1] On December 6, 1961, Mr. and Mrs. Dower were in my study to pass on the final form of this story for the press. On turning out the light, Mr. Dower and I saw Mrs. Dower's left hand glowing with a pale-green light, and streams of light passing from her fingers toward the extended fingers of her right hand. (See p. 39.)

[2] J. B. Van Helmont in the sixteenth century taught that "a magnetic fluid radiated from men and could be guided by their wills to influence directly the minds and bodies of others," and Valentine Greatrakes (born in Ireland, 1628) was known as "the stroking doctor" because he possessed this strange power to heal.

human task to change from lip-reading to hearing and we are told that many people never achieve it. But isn't it thrilling to be able to call to her when she is upstairs—and at one time we had to stamp our foot on the floor to attract her attention just across the room!

Other "miracles" keep continuing. Some of the cures and improvements seen recently couldn't be called by any other name. It is amusing to hear of doctors saying, "I'm sure it was broken," [3] and checking up again on X-ray plates!—or wondering what has suddenly happened to so-called "powdered discs"!

Yours very sincerely,
(Signed by the patient's father)

Having followed this case for over eight years I feel that I can be delivered from the charge of pretending that only a temporary improvement was achieved.

A letter received from Mrs. Dower dated December, 1961, contains the following:

Three weeks ago, we saw the aural-training mistress of the school Christine attended between the ages 3-11, and showed her Christine's most recent audiometer graph. She compared it with the graphs made from tests which she, herself, had given over the years, and her comment was that she would now grade Christine as "severely deaf" whereas before, she was graded as "profoundly deaf." There are four categories: partially deaf, severely deaf, profoundly deaf and totally deaf; so you see she has been up-graded. We discussed the case fully with her and although she pointed out that some of Christine's improved response to sound could be attributed to the fact that she is now making more use of her

[3] This quotation refers to a patient with a broken wrist treated by Mrs. Dower. After ten days no sign of the fracture could be found even with X rays.

residual hearing, *that alone* could not account for *all* the improvement.

One thing which has delighted us is Christine's growing love of music! When she comes home for holidays, she is only in the house a few minutes before her record player is in use. Her taste is wide and includes "rock" as well as classical. When she first showed this interest in music, we thought she perhaps enjoyed the vibration rather than the sound, but we now know that she can really hear for she can recognise her favourites when she hears them elsewhere (e.g., on the radio or television). Also, she can hear and enjoy music when played very softly—in fact, she seems to prefer it. It is strange to have her complain about people who have their radio and television sets on "too loud"!

All that we have told you of what Christine can hear takes place when she is using a hearing aid. Without it, she can hear very little of normal sound—speech has to be louder than normal as has music; part of this is true because she has come to rely on her aid. When we remember that *she could not hear anything at all* without an aid when she first lost her hearing; and also that we were told that she would not be able to use a hearing aid; then, we realise what a miracle has been and is being wrought! In the early days, it was difficult even to attract her attention, and to keep her "au fait" with what was happening around her, so that she did not feel isolated or frustrated, was only achieved by constant, patient attention. At the beginning of her healing, we remember how she hated sound, —"Noise is awful" was her cry! And now she is more and more anxious to hear and so thrilled at every step forward. In a letter from school some time ago, she wrote, "I can now hear the records when I am in the next room." . . .

You will be interested to hear that she feels a call from God to serve on the mission field. She did not tell us until she felt quite sure that God was asking this of her and her only concern is to see *how* God can use her in this way. Her handicap will prevent her from being a doctor or teacher—but she is keen on biology and general science and it may be that she will be able to do laboratory work in a mission hospital—we shall see!

We shall indeed. It does look as though odic force has achieved a degree of improvement which otherwise would not have been attained.

VI

The Case of
MRS. MOORE

WHEN MRS. MOORE WAS SHOWN INTO MY ROOM MORE THAN twenty years ago, she looked far too young to be called "Mrs." but so attractive that her married state could occasion no surprise. She brought a letter from her doctor with her, so, having had no time to read it, I asked her what I could do to help her. She leaped to her feet with an almost startling alacrity, and, with an equally startling gesture, almost tore open her pretty pink blouse and displayed, on an otherwise perfect skin, one of the most unsightly rashes I have ever seen. It covered the whole of her chest from shoulder to shoulder, crept down over her bosom and upward on to her neck. Big "nettle-rash" blisters burned angrily there, and it was not hard to believe her when she spoke of sleepless nights with the irritation and of frustration and annoyance in that the wearing of an evening dress or even a normal summer frock was impossible. "The annoying thing is," she said, "that I start off from the house with no sign of any trouble, and by the time I've walked into the town, I look like this. The doctor says it must be psychological, so I have come to you."

Fastening up her blouse, Mrs. Moore, tearful and angry, sat back in the chair and sincerely tried to relax and quietly tell me her story. In this kind of work I used to try to get the patient to begin at the beginning of a story. It still seems to me quite a reasonable place to begin! But I have learned by experience that a troubled person wants to begin with the most disquieting and uppermost factor in his or her mind, and that, frequently, is the annoyance or pain or inconvenience of the present symptom.

So I listened to the stories of how Betty Moore, who was only twenty-two-and-a-half, had missed this party, had had to leave that dance, had turned back on her way to have tea with a friend, and, very impressively, had once had to come out of church.

"So you do go to church," I cut in.

"Oh, yes. I've always been taught to do so," she said. "I was brought up in a Christian home. I actually taught in a Sunday school for a time—with the very little ones, of course."

"And now?" I asked.

Then came a torrent of tears.

When the storm had subsided, a very, very queer story emerged. Betty Moore had been married about eighteen months. She had been brought up, she told me, as a Baptist and, she added, "I was converted when I was fifteen, although now I think it was just an emotional experience brought about by a very good-looking young evangelist who came to our church. All my friends were 'converted,'" said Betty, "and I went with them into the vestry and signed my name in a book."

At seventeen or eighteen she met Ronald, and at twenty-one she was married. Then came a most unlooked-for complication. Betty was a warm, affectionate girl and passionate in her loving. Ronald was not only restrained but sexually cold, inept, and ignorant. Betty wonders now whether the restraint was because Ronald knew he would have to go into the army and did not want the complication of children, or even that of arousing his wife and then leaving her for long periods of time. They did not quarrel. They were fairly happy and went about a lot together, but Betty was physically unsatisfied.

Then came the dreaded moment when Ronald departed for war service, and Betty went back to the little home to take up her life again. It was a lonely life and the house was situated in a lonely spot, for although it was on a main road and buses passed the door, it was between a village and a small country town, without the amenities of either. She had liked it at first. It was lovely to be there with Ronald by the cozy fire on the long winter nights, listening to the radio. Even more attractive were the fine summer evenings, as they worked together in the little garden which was already gay with flowers and in which Ronald had constructed a rustic arbor, concealed from passers-by, where they could sit together and watch the sun go down behind the distant hills. But now its loneliness got on her nerves. She invited friends in and had them to stay, but she clearly could not always be doing that, and sleeping alone was a torment. She came to dread the nights, hating the sight of the bedroom, thinking quite early in the day, "I know I shan't sleep again tonight," until at last a stubborn insomnia took hold of her. She would toss and read a bit, get up and make tea, read again and put the book down, and get through the night somehow; but healthy, refreshing sleep eluded her.

Like a wise girl, she went to the doctor in the town. He was young and attractive. So was she. She knew at once that he liked her. She also knew that she liked him. He gave her sleeping tablets, and she began to sleep and was very grateful. But it did not end there. She made excuses to go and see him. She delighted in being examined by him and they became more and more intimate.

Mrs. Moore found it easier to write some of her story down, and I quote now from these letters.

He started to call round here once every now and then, dropping in for a morning cup of coffee, or an afternoon cup of tea, and I loved those short visits. We were by then good friends, and I was always tremendously glad to see him popping in. Then one evening about seven o'clock came a knock at my door. It was November and pitch-black when I opened the door. To my surprise it was "he." He said that he was on his way to a case and being perished had looked in for a coffee. Honestly I can say that never for a single moment did I see any wrong in his popping in like that. I was surprised he had called at night, but surprise was all I felt, truthfully. Well, he didn't stop very long, about twenty minutes, and then I went to the front door to let him out. There in the darkness he took me in his arms. It was a surprise I can assure you, although I knew by then that I cared deeply for him. Well, need I go on? To my everlasting sorrow on one hand, and to my everlasting joy on the other, he swept me off my feet, and for the first time I became a woman in that brief bitter-sweet time that followed. I asked him not to carry on, twice, but with his arms around me, and my heart doing mad things I never knew could happen, I surrendered. He left me telling me that soon he'd come back.

I sat long hours into the night after he had gone, being amazed and ashamed at myself for letting such a thing happen, and yet mixed with those feelings were ones of deep happiness and I was glad that he whom I loved had shown me the way to love. I seemed to have found a deep affection for my husband rather like a mother's love, I imagine, but this new-found love was something in my heart and life that I never knew could exist on earth.

89

And then when I awoke the next day, I was so awed by my fearful sin that I ran away. I knew that if I stayed, just the sight of him would be enough for me to weaken, so I went away for some weeks. You see, if only I wasn't a believer, it would and could be so easy. I shouldn't hesitate, but go running to him, asking forgiveness and giving all that I could give to him; I know life would be wonderfully happy then. But my Christian beliefs hold me back. "What have I done to my Lord?" I keep thinking. "Shall I ever be forgiven?" Then comes the evil thought: "Oh forget all that and go to the love of your heart, be loved. The war may kill either one of you soon." Then again comes the thought, "How could I possibly meet my God with such a blot on my life?"

Do you see my tormenting problem? Could the hell of a life led in guilty conscience be worse than the hell I've been through since last November? I haven't re-started the situation between us mainly because of my Christian faith, I suppose, and also because I should hate to do anything that would hurt my husband. He is now in the Middle East, so you see how simple things could be if I'd let them, and all of me longs for this love of mine, not only physically, but for his company and his smile. Did I do right in doing what I did, or can I with any chance re-start that glimpse of heaven that I found in November?

I have lived in torment ever since November. Sometimes I think one way, then another. One day I think that when the war ends, and if my husband is spared, all will be well if only we have children after his return. I'm passionately fond of little ones, and although I should wish they were "his," maybe I could settle down if my husband and I had a little one. Then the next day I feel I can't go on any longer unless I see this love of my heart and spend the rest of my days with him, if he'd have me, which I doubt, for he's a gay lad, and I doubt even if it were possible if he'd marry me. He might do. I can't be sure, but anyway I wasn't the first or last, I'm sure of that.

90

So after months of being nearly driven mad, I turn to you. My religion doesn't seem to mean to me what it did, and I'm worn out with trying to find a way. Can you help me? Oh if you can, please do. Your name seemed to come into my mind several times lately when I was trying to see my way clear, and so I beseech you, if you can give me advice, please do.

In a further letter she wrote:

If I've struck you as empty-headed, foolish and thoroughly undeserving, then please just put this letter on the fire and forget I ever wrote, but if in your heart you can find a little pity for a tortured human being, then please tell me what to do, I pray. I've been working very hard as a nurse since November in one of our busy hospitals. I love the work and hope to continue. Perhaps the harder I work, the more I shall see that I took the right course, and can only hope now for my Lord's forgiveness. I feel a beast at times to have betrayed my husband like I did. How could I forget my sacred marriage vows, and yet he bewitches me, and I know that if "he" asked me I'd go with him tomorrow, marriage or no marriage. Why do we always love the rogues, I wonder, instead of the good, stolid, loving husbands?

I enclose a stamp for your reply. Help me if you can, I beg of you, and if you can, thank you with all my heart.

I felt that I had better have a talk with the doctor. I wrote him a line and he came up to London to see me. He was a very nice fellow, and was so frank and honest with me that my heart warmed to him. He had his own problems, too, and needed some help, but that is another story. If the facts had become public, I suppose he would have been struck off the medical register, but if that had been done, the public would have lost a very good doctor whose secret, as far as I know, is known only to Mrs. Moore, her husband, and myself, and none of us will ever disclose the fact that repeatedly he slept with his beautiful young patient in her lonely house near a distant country village. The doctor himself was very repentant. He went into one of the forces and, after our interview, never saw Mrs. Moore again.

Mrs. Moore sold her house and went to live with her mother in the village. All the main shopping had to be done in the town. We found after some time that the rash only occurred if she went to the town! This will sound fantastic to many readers, but the facts seem to point in the following direction. In imagination, the reader can see Mrs. Moore living with her mother in the village. The mother, a very respectable and respected person, knows nothing of what has been going on. No one in the neighborhood knows the story. Mrs. Moore is trying to forget the doctor, and to forget all that had happened. Yet as the letters quoted reveal, she is far from penitent. If the doctor had not removed himself, she would have gone on being intimate with him. But although she has written regularly to Ronald, she feels terribly guilty where he is concerned.

In the life which she seeks to make as busy and as full as she possibly can, she can forget guilt, and that emotion of feeling guilty she is beginning to repress. Now repression means that an emotion is pushed down into the deep mind so successfully that it ceases to worry consciousness *in that form.* In other words, the guilt was becoming unconscious.

But, in order to understand Betty, another psychological law must be remembered. If the deep mind is asked to hold within itself an emotion which is inimical to its well-being, it tries to evade this strain by passing it on to the body. We find a number of people ill whose symptoms are in the body, but the cause of whose symptoms lies in the state of the emotions. I have given instances elsewhere[1] in which hate, resentment, jealousy, worry, malice, and guilt become translated into physical symptoms. It is as though the deep mind—which is more sensitive than the body—said to it, "I cannot carry this burden any more, you must take it." It is often noticed in such a patient that when the body does thus take on itself an illness, the patient becomes much less strained in mind. It is easier to bear pain of body than pain of mind. (Another good reason for repenting before death ends the life of the body but not the mind.) Moreover, subconsciously the patient knows he ought to be punished, and the physical illness gives him that relief.[2] He punishes himself with illness.

The choice of symptom made by the unconscious mind is a difficult matter still being widely discussed, and would take us farther than this simple story warrants. Sometimes the mind just uses a tendency toward some particular illness in the patient. It fastens on a congenital or hereditary weakness, or continues an illness which began in a completely materialistic way, such as a broken leg that will not knit together, an indigestion that grumbles on and on, or even a cold that does not clear up. But sometimes the symptom itself is a kind of mimicry of the emotional condition repressed in the mind. Thus, one patient I knew, terrified in the war that a beam or ceiling would fall on him, developed a tic or involuntary twitch like a man dodging a falling beam. This twitching overtook him whenever he felt frightened or anxious about anything.

It occurred to me to wonder whether Betty's stain of mind had been translated, through the familiar workings of the un-

[1] See Psychology, Religion and Healing, op. cit.
[2] See Ibid., pp. 316 ff.

93

conscious mind, into a stain of body. She had certainly "got something on her chest." She had, quite naturally and rightly, consulted an eminent dermatologist. He had treated her in every way known to medical science. He was fully aware that many skin conditions were set up by emotional situations and he asked her if she were worrying about anything. Alas! she told him nothing about her worries at all. There are some patients who find it easier to confide in a doctor than a minister of religion. There are others just the opposite. "I feel I could tell you," they say, "but I couldn't possibly tell anyone else." If she had been a Roman Catholic and had gone to confession and told her story to the priest, I think all would have been cleared up. If she had gone to her minister, he could have dealt just as ably and adequately with the situation. It was that bottling up and that refusal to recognize "sin" as sin that had produced repression and its physical "somatization," or translation into the bodily symptom of the unsightly rash.

With Betty's permission, since she was getting very much "under the weather," I obtained special "compassionate leave" for her husband and he came home. With courage and complete candor, Betty told him the whole story. Ronald had developed wonderfully in the army. In every sense his nature had broadened and deepened. Morally he had kept himself to himself and he had found a religion which had given his previously fettered nature complete release. He was impatient of the barriers that separate denominations, but the essentials of a life-giving, liberal Free-Church Christianity he had certainly found.

He forgave Betty at once, completely and finally. They decided never to mention the matter again. I can see them now sitting together in my London study in which there was a simple altar with a cross on it. After we had talked a little, Betty said a most interesting thing to me. "Would you mind," she asked, "going through the marriage service with us here and now? I want to make my vows all over again."

She took off her wedding ring and handed it to me. I lighted two candles which symbolize the Light of the World who seeks to dispel all our darkness, and there we three knelt for a time in silence before the cross which symbolizes the self-giving Love that never lets any of us go. Then, reverently and quietly, we went through the service, and almost inaudibly, tears running down her face, Betty whispered the responses—"for better, for worse, for richer, for poorer, in sickness and in health, till death do us part. . . ." Ronald put the ring on her finger and we said some prayers and I walked out of the room and left them alone. . . .

Gratitude is the best payment any of us can ever have and Betty did not forget to pay. Having quoted her own words earlier, I will quote from a letter before me now, though its date is 1941:

I have been making enquiries about "service abroad" with the Red Cross. Evidently help is urgently needed and I think I shall decide to go. I shall dread the journey, but once that is over, it won't be so bad. I don't think there is more than one chance in a million that I shall get anywhere near Ronald [3] as I believe I come under military authorities, and they certainly won't bother about fixing up husbands and wives at a place near one another! Still, I shall always go on hoping, and I hope for the rest of my life to do all I can to make Ronald an even happier man than he was before. It is easy to say that now, I suppose, but then I must do so, for I

[3] I have altered the name, of course.

shall always feel that I've cheated, and if he did but know, hurt him beyond forgiveness.

I do hope you will forgive this long letter, but I felt I must write and tell you how I was feeling now. It was more than good of you to spare me time from your very busy life. I was and always shall be so very, very grateful for your help. I had no one else to turn to, and how glad I am that I came to you. I don't think I'll ever forget that little room, and our talk. I knew definitely after seeing you that there was only one way for me to take, and God helping me, may I go on through life now with a deeper purpose and a firmer resolve to live up to the name of Christian.

Thank you once more with all my heart.

Later I saw Betty again, radiant, serene, loved, and happy. She was a delight to look at. She was wearing the same pretty pink blouse. She looked at me with mischievous, dancing eyes; "Do you want to see my chest?" she said. But it was quite unnecessary. She had "got something off her chest" forever and it was swallowed up in the mercy and love of God. The rash never returned, and after twenty years the word "cure" can surely be used. Any Christian in whom she had confided could have helped her to achieve deliverance, but I was glad she had come my way. Ronald's forgiveness had been but the forerunner of her acceptance of God's forgiveness, and I had, in the case of Betty Moore, one more illustration of a statement I made elsewhere[4] that the forgiveness of God is the most powerful therapeutic idea in the world.

Many physical symptoms are physically caused, and to regard every physical symptom as a sign of some spiritual malaise, let alone sin, would, in my opinion, be very unfair and usually

[4] See *Psychology, Religion and Healing*, op. cit., p. 334.

96

inaccurate. At the same time, no one who knows what guilt can do and what God can do, is surprised that a paralyzed boy could take up his mat and walk when he felt, soaking into the very depths of his mind, all the love and understanding and renewing power which poured from Jesus when he said, "Laddie,[5] thy sins are forgiven thee."

---

[5] The word Jesus is reported to have used is a word of endearment. Paul used it when he wrote to young Timothy.

VII

The Case of

BOBBIE FORREST

IT WAS A MINISTER WHO TOLD ME FIRST ABOUT BOBBIE, HIS brother, and his parents. They all went together to church, but the minister, the Rev. Charles Rutren, was troubled about Bobbie. He was one of the most attractive kiddies Rutren had ever had to deal with, but he had a kind of faraway look about him—almost as if he were drugged.

So one afternoon the minister called and asked Mrs. Forrest if Bobbie were well. She was quite ready to tell the story, and here it is.[1]

Bobbie was born in a blitz. Few people who did not go through it realize what happened in London in the winter of 1940 and the spring of 1941. Night after night the warning siren went at sunset and the "all-clear" did not sound until dawn. Through the long nights Londoners by the thousands slept in the stations of the underground railway. Thousands of others found some spot of comparative safety according to their means. The wealthy who did not disappear into the country every night dug—or rather had dug for them—refuges deep under their own gardens. The poor had "Anderson shel-

[1] Mrs. "Forrest" has read this account and confirmed the accuracy of the events and of the psychological and spiritual factors.

98

ters." Some went to the cellars of mission halls or the crypts of churches. Some shored up the safest room in their own homes, took out the window glass (a most terrible and common cause of ghastly mutilation), built blast walls, boarded up the windows, and hoped for the best.

When one thinks of Mrs. Forrest, her husband away in the service, with a boy of six years of age and herself "expecting," one remembers the words of Christ when he prophesied the fall of Jerusalem: "Woe unto them that are with child and to them that give suck in those days! And pray ye that your flight be not in the winter" (Matt. 24:19).

On a night of horror and terror and noise Bobbie was born into this mad world to the accompaniment of bombs and anti-aircraft guns. The first light he saw was not the gentle dawn, but the London sky bright red with the glare from a burning city. His mother was thirty-eight years of age at the time, and had been married nine years. Was it likely that the health of a little child should be unaffected by an entry into the world under such conditions? Many exaggerated stories have been told of the effect on the unborn child of any shock to the mother who carries him. But when the fears of a sensitive woman increase as her pregnancy develops, and when the hour of birth is one which would terrify any man or woman in the world, one would hardly expect freedom from consequences in the newly born. Yet for nearly three years all went well. When Bobbie was two years of age, a flying bomb dropped at the end of the road in which the Forrests lived, and Mrs. Forrest remembers being very frightened and covering Bobbie's head with a pillow to protect his face from flying glass splinters. Still, nothing seemed to distress him except the sound of loud bangs. Then the blow fell. The "fits" began.

Wisely, the doctor was summoned. He made a diagnosis at once but wisely waited, before telling Mrs. Forrest, to have his diagnosis confirmed at the Great Ormond Street Hospital for Children. The encephalogram was interpreted as showing that little Bobbie, three years of age, was suffering from minor epilepsy, or petit mal.

They were not bad attacks. He vomited, was incontinent, and lost consciousness for a brief spell. When he regained it, he felt dizzy and tired. As far as the parents know, he has never had any fits in his sleep. He has always slept well, except that he took a long time to "go off." The family doctor continued to treat these fits, and the attacks were infrequent.

I came into the picture at the end of February, 1953. Bobbie was then nearly twelve years of age, and his brother was eighteen. There are only two children. Mr. Rutren, the minister, was in my study discussing another matter when he told me about Bobbie and asked if I would see him. We fixed up a convenient date and Bobbie came with his mother. I was as attracted to the boy as Rutren was. First of all, I confirmed the facts from the mother, and found that the attacks were becoming more frequent. Two had occurred very near together, and a certain amount of alarm was being felt by the parents. At this time Bobbie was having three luminal tablets and two tablets of sodium amytal in every twenty-four hours. No wonder he had a faraway look as if he were drugged, and no wonder that his teacher complained that though an attractive and well-mannered boy, he was slow in regard to his school work.

Then I had a long talk with Bobbie. He was not in the least shy. He chatted happily about school life and especially games. His favorite master was the one who taught him physical training and who refereed at the football matches. He worried a bit about his school work, especially his mathematics. Then I asked him what he was most afraid of. He puckered up his brows a bit and then said that his greatest fear was that his elder brother, James, would have to go into military service and might "go to Korea and get shot." I felt that this was not a fear severe enough to set up epilepsy.

I took Mrs. Forrest to one side then, and asked her if I might hypnotize Bobbie in her presence and ask him some questions under hypnosis. I explained to Mrs. Forrest that sometimes the emotion of fear adhering to an experience, or a group of experiences, which had fallen to the bottom of the pond of the mind, disturbed that mind in curious ways. Mud at the bottom of a pond might send up bubbles of gas to the surface. Not much can be learned from a bubble as to its cause far below the surface of a pond, and not much can be learned from an epileptic fit of what is causing it; but, physical causes apart, there might be psychological disturbance in the deep mind through events which were "forgotten" (amnesia) and yet which still had a life of their own at the bottom of the mind with fear attached to them, fear in a state of compression that was bound to find some way of release and chose this kind of "fit" as its attempt at finding release.

To change the figure, one might have an abscess or wound deep in the body which discharged pus into the bloodstream and continued to set up symptoms of all sorts until the abscess was opened up and cleaned and there was no longer in it any pus to be discharged.

I guessed that in Bobbie's deep mind, normally unrecoverable to consciousness, there lay the memories of the air raids that had terrified him in his very early days. Indeed, there is evidence—I have had some in my own experiences—to prove that the mind can, under certain conditions, remember the actual experience of being born. Certainly the mind *never* forgets any experience. When we say we have "forgotten," we only mean that we cannot, by an act of will, bring to the surface and recover to consciousness the memory of some particular experience. Under hypnosis it can be remembered. We are told by those who are rescued from near drowning that early "forgotten" incidents can be recalled, but hypnosis is safer! Once remembered, the bottled-up emotion inherent in the memory can be released. It is that repressed emotion that is so important.

The critic might argue, "Surely it is better to let a child forget the terrible bombing. Is that not Nature's own way of curing? It seems terrible to recall such horrors to the memory." This sounds convincing, but it is dangerously false. We do not allow a broken arm to heal without being sure that it is properly "set." Nature would allow it to set in a position which would render it useless. Nor do we leave a dirty wound to Nature without first cleansing it. If emotional health is to be safeguarded and recovery quickened, we must be certain first that the situation to be "forgotten" does not contain a factor which will cause further trouble. Two men may be struck in the chest with shrapnel and it may penetrate the lung. Let us imagine that in one case the shrapnel is clean, and in the second case dirty or contaminated with other matter. In the first case the lung tissue will harden round the shrapnel and the latter may not even have to be extracted. The wound heals and gives no further trouble. The lung will, as it were, shut that bit of itself up in hardened tissue and put it out of action, carrying on with the remaining lung tissue. But in the second case, suppuration may well take place and pus be formed and a situation caused which will necessitate surgery. If surgery is not resorted to, the wound continually gives trouble.

With his mother's permission and in her presence I hypnotized Bobbie. He was a splendid subject for this form of treatment, which I have described elsewhere.[2] Then, warning his mother not to be alarmed, I asked Bobbie this question, "Now tell me what, deep down, you are afraid of." Without a fraction of a second's pause he uttered in a half sob the one word, "Bombs!" and then broke into a torrent of tears. He was still, of course, under hypnosis. Then, with amazing vividness and accuracy, he described the bombing and remembered his mother carrying him to safety. He expressed the fears which for so long he had repressed. The most significant of them was the fear that his mother, who had placed a pillow over his face to shield it from flying glass, was, in fact, trying to suffocate him, to get him out of the way. This was hard for a loving mother to believe but, of course, at the time of the bombing she could not stop to explain, and the misunderstanding is easy to account for. "During the actual raids," his mother told me, "James, his elder brother, cried and sobbed, but Bobbie seemed much quieter at the time." He "bottled it up" to his own harm. At last emotion subsided, save that, as I pointed out to his mother, his mouth still twitched. A fit had, no doubt, accompanied the discharge of emotion.

When the storm subsided, I told Bobbie, still hypnotized, that the war was over, that bombs would never be dropped near him again, that his mother's unvarying love surrounded him, that he had got rid of his fears. His mind was clear. Since he was an enthusiastic attender of the local Sunday school, I

[2] *Psychology, Religion and Healing*, op. cit., pp. 109 ff.

had something to go on and I could use religion as it ought to be used. I told him that Jesus, who was a finer captain than even Mr. —— —the footballer he so admired, and the sports master at school—had chosen him to be in his special team and was counting on him to play the game. Then I told him he would wake up with a grin and tell me again about the bombing. I wakened him telling him, as I normally do wake a person from the hypnotic sleep, that when I counted ten he would awaken feeling much better, on top of the world, full of joy and confidence. Bobbie sat up brightly and repeated the story with some, but with far less emotion than had been apparent during the hypnosis.

I saw him again two months later, in April. His mother said there had not been a single fit, so with the doctor's consent we decided to halve the luminal. I saw him again in August. There had been no fit of any kind. The boy was reported brighter at school and much happier at home. With the family doctor's approval I suggested one luminal at night only. I saw him again in January, 1954. Again the mother reported no fits and that Bobbie was happy and "easier to live with." At this point, with the doctor's consent, we decided to drop all drugs unless an exciting experience such as a birthday party had to be coped with.

A year went by without fits and we began to hope that the evil demon had been driven out. Of course, it may be that the child never had epilepsy at all, though the encephalogram seemed definite.

I have long suspected that what is sometimes labeled epilepsy, and what faithfully produces the symptoms of epilepsy, may be a psychological illness using "fits" of some kind or another—call them what we will—to discharge emo-

104

tion which is under pressure in the deep mind. Dr. W. Barker has written on "The Petit Mal Attack as a Response Within the Nervous System to Distress in Organism-Environment-Integration." Indeed, perhaps this kind of attack should be labeled a form of epilepsy, but if so, perhaps it should be treated by psychotherapy rather than by years of drugs. The danger seems to me that young people may be labeled "epileptic" and drugged for the rest of their lives and advised not to marry or take up a desired profession, while all the time their troubles could possibly be ended as easily as those of Bobbie.

As this book goes to press I find that Bobbie is looking forward to his twenty-first birthday. His mother says three years have passed since he had a single "attack." We can only hope and pray that he has achieved complete freedom from his disability.

I should like to illustrate my theme in this chapter by relating the story of Colin Fellows. You must imagine a tall, slender lad, fair-haired, delicate, very sensitive, musical, and artistic—a familiar type who, one feels, was not made for the rough and tumble of life. Yet he wanted to go up to Cambridge when he was old enough and study law and enter that profession, which was his father's. But, alas, a tragic death deprived him of his father, and his mother was brokenhearted. Though Colin was only fourteen at the time she relied on him for support and, in my opinion, leaned on him more heavily than she should have done on one so young and sensitive. There were three younger children, far too young to sustain the mother, and one can sympathetically feel for her that she must talk to someone. Alas, while Colin had to bear her tears and laments, her queries and sometimes her outbursts of bitter resentment, Mrs. Fellows never told him the whole truth about his father's death. The truth was that Mr. Fellows had got into some predicament which threatened his standing as a lawyer and, in a moment of panic and despair, had taken his own life. Colin did not know that, and here probably the mother thought she was doing the right thing in keeping the matter from him.

But on one terrible evening, Colin came in quietly at the front door and heard voices in the living room, the door of which was open. He was not the kind to eavesdrop, but his mother was giving way to passionate sobbing in front of a friend of the family who had come to comfort her. "You can rely on me," Colin heard the friend say, "no one will ever hear the word 'suicide' from my lips."

Poor Colin! If he had burst into the room and said, "I heard what you said and I demand to know the truth," perhaps less psychological harm would have been done to him. But he kept it to himself. Perhaps he feared being called an eavesdropper. Perhaps he respected his mother's earlier silence. Boys in their early teens do not think things out. But in his heart there was created at that moment a vast pool of resentment. His mother, in his opinion, had cheated. She sought his comfort, but had never given him her confidence. She leaned on him and yet left him in the dark. He maintained his silence and became morose and anxious and unhappy, symptoms of the repressed emotions in his heart.

While he was preparing for the grueling tests which any boy faces who wants to get a scholarship to the university, the enemy struck. He had what was later called an epileptic fit and fell to the ground. When this had happened several times, it was clear that he would never be able to go to Cambridge and follow the chosen career of the law. The doctor did all he knew and no criticism of his treatment can be even suggested, but at this stage the matter was brought to my attention, and since I had known both Colin's parents and liked and admired the boy, I asked him to make the journey to London to see me. By this time I knew all the facts and I told Colin everything he wanted to know. I encouraged him to express in words his resentment against his mother. He became quite aggressive. In my room he walked about, his fists clenched, his eyes blazing, his hot words shouted across my little room. "I could have taken it," he said between teeth clenched in his anger, "but she treated me like a kid. Poor old Dad, I know just how he felt"—and very much more not worth printing. Then I hypnotized him and told him to get off his chest anything else he wanted to express by way of aggression. Nothing new emerged save another emotional outburst of resentment. It was his last "fit," or, as I would prefer to call it, emotional storm. The night before his finals he had a momentary blackout, but he has had nothing of the kind since. That never-to-be-forgotten abreaction in my rooms took place twenty years ago, and since then Colin has married and has his own family. I think we can now use the word "cure." He is a lawyer and I still meet him once a year or so, and we chat about the old, evil days when it looked as though all was up and that a sentence of daily drugging for life would have to be served, in the setting of a frustrated, celibate, and comparatively wasted life.

Of course, he may never have had epilepsy. No one seems to know clearly what it is, or what causes it, or what cures it. The word means "seizure," and, says the British Epilepsy Association, "the cause is obscure." Advertising in the London Times (May 14, 1962), the association said that more was known about the moon than about epilepsy. It has been called a "short circuit in the brain," or an electrical storm in the brain, or a sudden discharge of nervous energy, but why the same stimulus should give A epilepsy and leave B exempt is not easy to discover. In the City Temple Psychological Clinic we have had several cases which make us wonder whether repressed aggression against a beloved person whom the patient dare not, must not, or will not hurt, does not lead to the kind of "fit" so readily labeled "epilepsy," and indeed showing as such on the encephalogram.

Another young man after years of "fits" has not had one for four-and-a-half years following such procedure as I have outlined. A young girl has gone two-and-a-half years during which time she undertook a fairly exciting trip abroad. A schoolgirl has gone a year without trouble, and when I first wrote out this chapter, I was trying to help a robust fellow of twenty-five who had been having several fits a day, and for whom the dependence on female relatives who "boss" him had been a cause of deep resentment and aggression. So far the longest freedom he has had has been a week, but even that has encouraged him and given him hope.

It would be foolish to write as if one had discovered a cure for epilepsy. Distinguished specialists who have made this disease their field for years have tackled the illness with far better understanding and success, and they have an equipment for their task far superior to mine, but in trying by psychological methods to help the few who have come my way, and who, for various reasons, have not been able to get more adequate help, I have been sufficiently encouraged to wonder if in some cases called epileptic, a psychological and spiritual approach might be successful where at any rate mere drugging has failed.[3] After all, the patient described in the Gospels[4] sounds like an epileptic, and after one final outburst he seems to have been made whole, though one only wishes one had the insight, the faith, and the spiritual power of the Master.

Dr. H. P. Newsholme claims that this case was not true epilepsy but "a repressed fear seeking relief in consciousness." [5] This description exactly fits the cases I have outlined above. We ought to note how carefully Jesus gets the "case history" of this patient from his father. (Mark 9:21 ff.) Jesus is not content merely to lay his hands on the patient. In other words, Jesus behaves far more like a modern doctor or psychologist than like a modern "faith healer."

---

[3] I was very interested in an article in the British Medical Journal of November 25, 1961, by Dr. D. A. Pond entitled, "Psychiatric Aspects of Epileptic and Brain Damaged Children," which contains the following sentence: "Epilepsy is a symptom, not a disease." Dr. Louis A. Gottschalk of Chicago has recognized the importance of a psychological as well as a physical approach to epilepsy. He writes, "The psychiatric study of genuine epilepsy has produced information which strongly suggests that psychological factors play a role in the elaboration or exacerbation of epileptic phenomena. . . . If psycho-pathological hypothesis of the origin of the epileptic syndrome have some basis in fact, there should be a possibility through psychological means of modifying the frequency and/or form of the seizures in certain epileptic patients." (Paper on the "Effects of Intensive Psychotherapy on Epileptic Children with a report on Three Children with Idiopathic Epilepsy," printed in the American Medical Association Archives of Neurology and Psychiatry, September, 1953, Vol. 70, pp. 361-84.)

[4] Mark 9:14-29; Matt. 17:14-20; Luke 9:37-43. See Psychology, Religion and Healing, op. cit., pp. 70 ff.

[5] H. P. Newsholme, formerly medical officer of health for Birmingham, England, in Health, Disease and Integration (London: Allen & Unwin, 1929), p. 131.

VIII

The Case of

MONICA COWLING

As I BEGIN TO WRITE THIS STRANGE STORY, I REALIZE THAT SOME
people will find it impossible to believe it. The names, of
course, are fictitious, as are all the names in this book. Other
unimportant details are invented to preclude identification,
but all the psychological and important facts are true.

During the last war, after the City Temple had been bombed
and I had no interview room, I was allowed, by the kindness of
one of the psychiatrists on the staff of the City Temple Psychological Clinic, to use a room in Harley Street. Into this
room one sunny afternoon walked a young lady who told me
one of the strangest stories I have ever heard, or am ever likely
to hear. She brought a letter from her doctor, who explained
in brief terms that she suffered from somnambulism (sleepwalking) and that he could do nothing for her but give her
drugs. He added that even if drugged, she now continued to
walk in her sleep unless the dose was made increasingly heavy.
In my mind's eye I can see the patient as clearly now as I could
on that summer afternoon over twenty years ago. She was of
medium height and her age was twenty-three. She was of
dark complexion and had very heavy "batwing" eyebrows and
very heavily reddened lips. She was not particularly beautiful,

110

but she had the steady kind of eyes that usually spell trust-worthiness. When one has interviewed people in trouble for over forty years, one—perhaps dangerously—comes to a fairly rapid conclusion as to whether they are speaking the truth or not. I trusted this girl from the beginning, and she turned out to be entirely worthy of trust.

I noticed at once, as one does, that she was married. When I asked her about her husband, I learned that he was on active service in the navy and away from this country on those dark, dismal, and dangerous journeys which Britain had undertaken in order to take to Russia the materials she needed in her fight against Hitler's armies. My patient missed her husband very much. They had not been married long. They had no children, but they very much wanted, as did thousands of other young married couples, to settle down and start a family. It became clear from what Mrs. Cowling said that sex desire, roused by the early days of her marriage, but unsatisfied through the absence of her husband, was a factor of great importance in her mental condition.

During this absence of her husband, Mrs. Cowling had gone back to her place of business and worked as private secretary to a "boss"—as she called him—who was indubitably kindness itself to her. She received good wages, was free all Saturday and Sunday, and on the other days of the week kept the usual office hours of nine to five-thirty. Indeed, the increasing kindness of the boss became another important factor in her condition. He grew fond of her, and, although married himself, took her out a good deal to supper, to theaters, to movies, and to dances, and she quickly realized that she was falling in love with him and that he sexually excited her. His embraces grew more and more intimate, and finally she went away and spent more than one night with him in an ecstasy of physical delight followed by a devastating attack of remorse and depression which sent her to her doctor, and finally, when the sleepwalking started, to me.

During her husband's absence she had returned to the very modest little home, in a poor street, in which her mother, who was a widow, lived. This was not so much a matter of deep affection as of convenience, for my patient and her husband had never had the time or the means to procure a house and the mother and daughter were company for one another. Sleeping alone in a house when bombs were dropping was not very attractive, as thousands who lived through the "blitz" would testify. The arrangement was also economical. The mother kept house and Monica, now Mrs. Cowling, went into the city each day to work, coming home at all hours of the night, and sometimes not returning at all. The mother, Mrs. Watson, was very deaf. Had this not been so, some of Monica's adventures might have been at least curtailed.

Monica (Mrs. Cowling) slept with her mother, not only in the same room, but in the same bed. Then Monica started getting out of bed, although sound asleep, and creeping downstairs and into the street. She went so quietly that her deaf mother, Mrs. Watson, never heard her go. Sometimes Mrs. Watson heard her daughter's return, but she never heard her departure until, much later, she kept awake on purpose to see what happened. Monica, it later transpired, went out into the street about two in the morning and returned shortly afterwards. Characteristically, like other sleepwalkers, she seemed to take less care in *returning* quietly and would bang a door even with violence, as if she did not care who heard her. Her nocturnal errand completed, secrecy was less important.

112

You can imagine Monica sitting in a Harley Street consulting room telling me that she woke up in the mornings tired out; that neighbors had heard noises in the night and complained to her mother; that one light-sleeping neighbor had seen her leave and return to the house and had drawn unpleasant conclusions; that she found mud on her shoes consistent with what she feared: namely, that she had become a somnambulist. The mother had then kept watch and could confirm the story. I was told that Monica and her mother had tried to cope with the situation. They had tied themselves to each other by the wrist, but Monica always succeeded in untying the knot without waking either her mother or herself. They had sometimes locked both the bedroom door and the front door and concealed the keys. Sometimes this had frustrated Monica and she had returned to bed or awakened. Sometimes, with uncanny cunning, she had found the necessary keys or duplicates. Mrs. Watson, the mother, had been told that it is dangerous to suddenly awaken a somnambulist, so she had not done so. Ideally she should have followed her daughter to see what happened, but she was afraid—and who can blame her? A London street at two in the morning during the wartime blackout, when an air raid might begin at any moment, is no place for a deaf old lady.

But another part of the story intrigued me immensely. Monica complained that a thief was visiting the house. She didn't suspect her mother. Indeed, some of the mother's things were missing. When asked who could have access to the house, Monica was silent. She couldn't think of anyone. No tradesmen had any opportunity. For myself, I could not help wondering why a thief should ever break into a house in a street like that in which the two women lived. He must have been,

I thought, a thief without much imagination. Cogitating on this, I had an inspiration. I asked Monica what things she had missed. She seemed at first reluctant to tell me. Then it emerged that the missing things of her own, supposed to have been stolen, had all been gifts which her husband had given her. As her birthdays had come round, he had, with admirable taste, given her cut-glass objects for her dressing table. But now the little tray had gone, then a powder bowl and its lid, then a perfume bottle, and so on. Finally, a very nice cut-glass vase had disappeared. Her mother had lost but little; a kitchen knife which had been her favorite potato peeler, and a photo frame of heavy brass, *given her by her son-in-law*, had been "stolen."

By this time the reader will have got a clue, particularly in view of the words printed in italics. It was easy to hypnotize Monica. Sleepwalkers are notably easy to hypnotize, and this I did. When she was deeply hypnotized I put to her this question: "When you walk in your sleep in the night, Monica, where do you take the things which you yourself have removed from your own dressing table and from the sitting room?" Without any hesitation came the answer of the deeply tranced patient: "I take them to the water tank at the end of our road and throw them in."

It will be remembered that during the war terrible fires were frequently started by falling bombs. In order that the men of the auxiliary fire service, who gave such splendid war service, should have sufficient water for their apparatus, a number of emergency water tanks were built on waste land, at road endings and junctions, and indeed at any convenient spot. Each of these held hundreds of gallons of water.

Monica awakened from the trance when told to do so, but

she had no memory of anything she had said during it. We arranged to meet in a few days' time, and she went home.

That evening, the officer in charge of the men in the auxiliary fire service for Monica's area, listened over the telephone to the strangest request of his lifetime. Having explained who I was, that I was about to ask him a preposterous favor, but that the granting of it would possibly restore the nervous health of a young woman, I asked him if he would be good enough to empty the water tank at the end of Tarry Street and bring me what he found at the bottom. His reply was natural enough. "Whose cat has been drowned?" he asked. I told him that at the bottom of the tank he would find a cut-glass tray, a perfume bottle, a powder bowl, a vase, a brass photo frame, and, I hoped, a potato knife. I was particularly anxious to find that knife because old Mrs. Watson was really so fond of it, and it had its own symbolism.

There were some difficulties to overcome with the firemen. Not only did emptying the tank mean wasting many hundreds of gallons of water, but "supposing there's a fire ten minutes after the tank is emptied?" However, I happened to know socially one of the "higher-ups." I had to tell him a good deal of the story. He thought I was mad. He said that he had always heard that those who deal with "nervy people" get like them, and so on. But in the end I got my way. One noon, when a bombing raid seemed unlikely, the tank was emptied. The missing articles were found. A grinning fireman, who had previously shared the opinions of his chief, brought them round in a bag which I took to Harley Street and hid under the desk.

In a few days Monica turned up for her appointment.

I said to her, "Monica, are you still in the employment of Mr. Lowther?"

She said, "Yes. Why?"

"It's a pity," I said. There was a long silence. Then I said, "You are twenty-three years of age, are you not?"

"Yes," she said. "You know that."

I said, "In seventeen years you will be forty."

"Yes," she said, "but what are you driving at?"

I said, "At forty, would you like to have a happy home with jolly children and a mind full of happy memories and no regrets, or would you choose to ruin your marriage, possibly smash your home, and spend your old age in remorse?"

Then the lightning fell. She rose up, white of face and every muscle tense.

"You've been talking to old Lowther," she said, "the old hypocrite!" She added a phrase which, if I remember rightly, was that he was "a loathsome toad." I told her that I had never seen Lowther, that I wouldn't know him if I saw him, that I knew nothing of him save what she herself had told me.

"Sit down quietly in that chair, Monica," I said, "and let's talk things out, because at the end of this interview you will be entirely cured of sleepwalking, and all the anxiety in your mind will disappear. I'm not talking to you merely as a parson," I added, "though I will do so if you wish it. In the meantime, see if you can follow this lecture on psychology which I'm going to deliver. I'll talk to you as if you were another person called just 'She.'"

Monica sank back in her armchair still white, and with a hint of angry tears in her eyes. She had a handkerchief at the ready and an expression of fear on her face. Then I began.

"She came into this room some weeks ago," I said, "because

her doctor sent her to get psychological treatment for her sleepwalking. She was honest from the first, and has never consciously lied, even to the last. What she didn't understand was that with her Christian upbringing and early training, her mind wasn't going to let her slip into wrongdoing without a struggle. Her symptoms are the signs of God's effort to keep her straight. Her husband was far away and she was lonely for love. Physical love had meant a lot to her, and what with one thing and another she began to feel that old Lowther's pawing and cuddling were better than nothing. It would ease her loneliness. Lowther's wife was an invalid, so she wasn't being cheated. Lowther finally persuaded her to go 'the whole hog' and thus got a satisfaction he had been denied for years, and she, Monica, got a satisfaction of a sort and no one was the wiser. But 'sin' opposes psychological as well as spiritual laws. It thwarts divine intentions, though we all do it. Every time she went into the parlor, there was that big photograph of her husband in the heavy brass frame that he had given her mother, and his face was so happy and radiant. She would come home from some Lowther adventure, look at the photograph, and feel miserable and ashamed and frightened. Then she would go to the bedroom to undress, and there were the lovely cut-glass objects that her husband had given to her, one for her birthday, one for Christmas, and so on. He was going to complete the whole set of toilet requisites in cut glass one of these days. Miserable and unhappy, she went to bed and fell asleep. But during sleep, as is always the case, her deep mind went on working. Then the devil, or, if you prefer it, the rebel part of her mind, whispered to her, 'Hundreds are doing what you are doing and there's no harm in it. You are silly to feel remorseful. Eric [the husband] will never find out. Perhaps he will be killed. What you should do is to get rid of the things that remind you of him. Get up now, dress, and collect some of them and throw them in the water tank at the end of the road. They'll never be discovered. You can say—if they are—that they've been stolen, and the thief must have thrown them there.' "

Monica roused at this. "It's a lie," she shouted. "They were stolen. I don't know where they are, and it isn't my fault if I walk in my sleep. I didn't come here to be insulted. As if I would take my own precious things that Eric gave me and throw them away—" The rest was a stormy torrent of tears.

"Now I'm going to be the parson," I told her. "Monica, you are much too good a girl to be happy on the road you've taken. This won't stop at sleepwalking. You'll have a bad nervous breakdown because your mind is in such a conflict. Go on as you are going on, and you'll ruin your own marriage, whatever you do to Lowther's. Even if Eric never finds out, your own mind will be full of bitter memories. It'll take you years to recover. But if you act now it is not too late. Tell Lowther you are not going to see him again. Get another job. I'll help you and in six months you'll be able to welcome Eric home on leave as a healthy, happy girl should. There's a happy home ahead for you and a mind saved from lifelong remorse."

She was silent a long time. "You are absolutely right," she said at last. "I suppose you are always right." (How little she knows!) "But," she added, "I honestly don't know where those things are that are missing, and how can I explain to Eric? Perhaps they really were stolen." I asked her if a burglar was likely to break into 42 Tarry Street and steal from her bedroom only those things that Eric had given her. "Besides,"

I added, rather enjoying the drama, "there won't be any explaining to do. All the things are here." I dragged out the fireman's bag from under the desk and we put the contents out on the desk. Monica's face was a picture. I laboriously tried to explain to her the workings of her own unconscious mind. It had sought to reduce the agony of conflict and conscience distress by getting her to remove, during sleep, those objects which constantly reminded her of the love of a faithful husband, risking his life for his country while she philandered with a married man for the sake of easing a temporary sexual hunger and stress.

When she had recovered from her first incredulous astonishment, Monica asked, "Why did I throw the knife away?" I could only guess at the answer. Perhaps her mother had suspected some "goings on" between her daughter and Lowther. Perhaps her daughter wanted unconsciously to punish her mother for some sharp word of criticism, and perhaps, one night as Monica walked in her sleep through the kitchen, she picked up the knife and threw it away. Is it fanciful to suppose that the mind of Monica saw in the knife the symbol of some "cutting" remarks the mother had made? I do not know. These things do happen in dreams, and sleepwalking is a kind of acted dream.

Always the somnambulist has a purpose in his walking. I once actually witnessed a somnambulist carry out a purpose which needed no Freudian analysis to interpret. Having gone to bed in a house full of people, he had fallen asleep and then walked, still asleep, into a room in which guests were still chatting by the fire, and he had got into a divan bed on the other side of the room. It was the bed in which a girl cousin, with whom he was in love, had formerly slept when she had suddenly turned up asking for accommodation for a night when all the bedrooms in the house were full. He was dreaming, and no one should think of him as immoral, for we do not control our dreams. So often the dream is the unconscious realization of a deep and unsatisfied hunger.

Here is another amusing case, though it had expensive concomitants. Mona, the wife of Dr. Murray, used to walk in her sleep and smash windows! Her husband naturally gave her sleeping pills, but they did not always prevent disaster. It was more than a little trying for a busy medical practitioner to have his night's rest broken by the smashing of glass and find his wife had left her bed to break, say, the bathroom window at two in the morning. A psychiatrist was consulted, but there were difficulties. In the first place he never sought the cause of her queer behavior, but only advised deeper sedation. Further, he was socially known to her, and had often co-operated with her husband, and Mona felt shy of telling him the whole story. I will not lengthen this chapter unduly by telling it here, but, of course, cure depends on finding out why the patient wants to perform the acts done during sleep, and indeed, on the patient's accepting that the alleged reason is a true one. Telling him or guessing at the reason will not do. The patient must realize why he acts as he does.

I append a letter from Mona:

Dear Dr. Weatherhead,

A very long time ago—a whole year in fact—you very kindly advised me about my unfortunate propensity for breaking windows in my sleep! I feel very ashamed that I have not written to thank you before now, and I should like to do so even though it was so long ago.

I thought you might also be interested—and perhaps amused!—

to know the remedy prescribed by the psychiatrist with whom I discussed the matter. He told me not to give the matter another thought, and if I felt tired or in any state conducive to sleepwalking to take a good sedative! I must confess that I was relieved to hear that he did not propose to psychoanalyse me, particularly as my husband is a colleague of his. They work together at the —— Hospital and one feels slightly foolish recounting sleepwalking activities to social acquaintances.

I may also add that since I saw you the last time I do not think I have stirred from my bed once, and writing to you helped me to get the whole thing into perspective and to regard it as the "mole hill" it seems to have been.

Thanking you again for your kindness,

Yours sincerely,

Mona Murray

I once treated a pretty young nurse who was under threat of dismissal by an irate hospital matron. The nurse had the habit of going to bed in the nurses' quarters, and then, while fast asleep, walking right across the hospital to a male ward and seeking to get into bed with the nearest patient. The unconscious desire was pretty clear and because it was unconscious involves no criticism of the patient's character. I heard of no complaints from the patients! The matron, however, felt that she was unfit to be a nurse. It was easy to cure her, and she became, and still is, a first-rate nurse. When the meaning of a dream is accepted by—not just told to—the dreamer, it no longer persists. Here lies the cure of nightmare and the cure of sleepwalking.

I don't know how much Monica told Eric when he came home on leave. That is not my business. I don't know how much deaf Mrs. Watson guessed. That is not my business either. I often wondered how Monica explained the recovery of that knife. Nor have I ever met Mr. or Mrs. Lowther. But I rejoiced in the way Monica Cowling not only awakened to what her mind was doing to her, but took action which brought her complete deliverance from somnambulism and the anxiety of which it was a warning symptom. She finished with the old life. In a new job she started afresh. She found immense release in the loving forgiveness of God. She found power and comfort in the transforming friendship of Christ. Psychology started the treatment. Religion completed it. It was lucky that she walked in her sleep, otherwise she would never have faced the moral problem in her life. And failing to face it, she would probably have ruined her own life, and other people's too. She seemed to me to illustrate once more the fact that we live in a *uni*-verse, not a *multi*-verse. Disharmony of all kinds, including all disease of mind and body, is an affront to the unity of the universe. It is something that should not be there. We are created to be good, and evil is an enemy of our health as well as of our peace of mind. Psychology and religion are handmaidens, not enemies. Good religion supports adequate psychology, and correct psychological technique never denies wholesome, unsectarian religion.

But this is not the place to theorize. All I can add is that it was heartwarming before I left the City Temple to look down from the pulpit and see Monica and her husband and two happy, healthy children singing a hymn we often sing at the City Temple.

> How sweet the name of Jesus sounds
>   In a believer's ear!
> It soothes his sorrows, heals his wounds,
>   And drives away his fear.

It makes *the wounded spirit* whole,
  And calms the troubled breast;
'Tis manna to the hungry soul,
  And to the weary, rest.

Eric has got a good civilian job now, and if ever two loving people made a happy Christian home, Eric and Monica have made one.

He makes the wounded spirit whole,
  And calms the troubled breast.

Sometimes psychology can help him. That sometimes seems to me its most worthwhile use.

IX

The Case of

MADGE DAVIES

IF I WROTE DOWN IN BLACK AND WHITE THAT I BELIEVED IN demons and that I thought it probable that there is not only one outstanding Devil, but hosts of evil spirits who affect the lives of men today, I expect some of my readers would shut this book and say, at least to themselves, "This man is mad. He is harking back to a superstition that science dislodged centuries ago, and as a modern, civilized, up-to-date reader I will read no more." Well, that is why I put this chapter near the end of the book! The reader had better get ready to shut it up. But first, if you are fair-minded, do consider a few interesting points.

Jesus Christ talked a great deal about devils. He claimed to cast them out and he commissioned his disciples to do the same. Is demon possession an old-fashioned name for what we now know as mental illness, schizophrenia, for instance, or obsessional neurosis? Or is there a residuum of illness that is not accounted for in this way?

It seems to me that if one accepts the New Testament, one is driven to a belief in devils unless one accepts one of the following hypotheses.

1. That Jesus was the child of his age in such matters; that

124

he did not know any better than anyone else; that his true humanity meant that he could go no farther than anyone else in regard to the extent of the knowledge then current.

But apart from the rather startling suggestion that in regard to the nature of any evil he did not know any better than anyone else, we find that, in fact, he *did* speak about evil spirits in a way quite different from his contemporaries, and thus was *not* the child of his age. For instance, they believed that devils existed in crumbs and they would not gather them up. Jesus ordered that they should be gathered up. (John 6:12.) His contemporaries believed that one should never accept as much as a drink of water from a foreigner, for devils lurked in the cup. Jesus *asked* for a drink from a foreigner. (John 4:7.) His contemporaries believed that evil spirits rested on unwashed hands—a useful, if superstitious, belief. The disciples of Jesus, *unrebuked by him*, brought down criticism on their heads by eating with unwashed hands. (Matt. 15:2.) Other examples could be given. The startling fact which emerges is that where Jesus behaves and speaks in a manner quite different from his contemporaries, yet in regard to some diseases—*not all, be it noted*—he speaks of men and women being possessed by devils and he makes a careful distinction, giving commandment to his disciples to heal all manner of diseases *and to cast out devils*.[1] The distinction at least suggests that demon possession was in a different category from disease.

2. It is sometimes said that Jesus was not the child of his day in such matters; that he knew better but that he made a

---

[1] Matthew uses a different Greek word for being possessed by a devil on the one hand, and being insane on the other.

125

concession to the beliefs of those to whom he was talking. But the points made above force one to ask why he did *not* make a concession to *all* the beliefs of his day.

3. Others have said that any person dealing with a disordered mind would not argue with a patient about the origin of his symptoms, but, for the time being, would accept the patient's own story so as to understand him the better and run no risk of antagonizing him. This is very important and very true, but Jesus talked of demon possession *when the patient was not present.*

Is it possible that Jesus believed that in certain cases a mind can be possessed by some evil entity, and that in that belief he was right?

At any rate, if the reader has not by this time closed this book and thrown it across the room, I would ask him to consider half a dozen points, and then, mentally adding them together, ask himself whether they do not "add up" to the possibility we are considering. After all, to dismiss any kind of phenomenon without pondering it and seeking to understand and explain it, is, as Fechner said, "to express our contempt for experimental science." My own feeling is not that we now know so much that we can dismiss a belief in evil spirits as part of the infantile thinking of the race; it is rather that we do not yet know enough to exclude the possibility of their existence.

1. Some time ago a man was hanged in England for the murder of two young girls whom he had raped. If I remember rightly, he told the judge, according to reports in the press, that he "would walk ten miles any day to rape a young virgin." Let us imagine, for the sake of the argument, that he did use

those words and that he never experienced either regret or repentance. What do we suppose happened to him? Death is not extinction. May he not have become in some sense an evil spirit? Would he not carry his sexual desires with him into the next world, where, deprived of a body, he could have no satisfaction? Is not that part of his hell? But is it conceivable that Satan, if he exists, would try to use him, to make him what Jesus once called a "twofold son of hell"? (Matt. 23:15.) Might he not seek to enter the body of a lustful man who is still on earth and bend him to his will? How often a man has said, after some moral lapse, "I was out of my mind," or, "I wasn't myself," or, "I can't imagine what I was doing," or, "I must have been out of my senses," or, "I don't know what possessed me to do such a thing."

This will seem wild theorizing to some modern readers. Let them then ponder the words of Kant:

I confess I am very much inclined to assert the existence of immaterial beings in this world, and to put my soul itself into that class. These immaterial beings form perhaps a great whole which may be called the immaterial world and it will be proved, I do not know where or when, that the human soul in this life is in indissoluble communion with all immaterial natures of the spirit world, on which it acts and from which it receives impressions.[2]

Dr. Elwood Worcester writes about discarnate spirits as if he met them every day. He says, "They imagine that the body of a living person into which they have entered is their own body, and they therefore, for a time at least, strongly resist all

[2] *Dreams of a Spirit Seer* (New Church Press), pp. 52, 61.

efforts to dispossess them." [3] Perhaps we are nearer the truth than we realize when we sing:

> Principalities and powers,
> Mustering their unseen array,
> Wait for thine unguarded hours
> Watch and pray!

2. What do we make of Paul's references in his letters? Do we brush them away as the superstitions of two thousand years ago? What does he mean by the "world rulers of this darkness," and "the spiritual hosts of wickedness"? (Eph. 6: 12.) What a lot one would give to know exactly what Jesus meant by "the dark Power has its way" (Luke 22:53 Moffatt.) When men like the late Archbishop Temple say, "I believe that he [Satan] exists and that a large share of responsibility [for human evil] belong to him *and to subordinate evil spirits*," [4] I do not myself stammer, "Tut! tut! what a lot of superstitious nonsense!" For I regard William Temple not only as a great scholar and a great saint but also as a great seer.

I find other men of education and insight saying similar things. F. W. H. Myers, for instance, is reported in *The Proceedings of the Society for Psychical Research* as saying, "The fact of possession has now been firmly established," and William James as saying,

The refusal of modern "Enlightenment" to treat "Possession" as an hypothesis, to be spoken of as even possible, in spite of the massive human tradition based on concrete experience in its favour, has always seemed to me a curious example of the power of fashion

---

[3] *Body, Mind and Spirit*, p. 96 (London: Hodder and Stoughton, 1931).
[4] *Nature, Man and God* (New York: St. Martin's Press, 1953).

in things scientific. That the demon theory will have its innings again is to my mind absolutely certain. One has to be "scientific" indeed to be blind and ignorant enough to deny its possibility.[5]

Roman Catholics are told they must believe in devils, and they have their official exorcists. Listen to Stöhr. In his Handbook of Pastoral Medicine he writes, "The possibilities of maladies caused by demoniacal influences must be accepted by every Catholic believer as a fact beyond doubt." Dr. James H. Hyslop, of the American Society for Psychical Research and editor of its Journal says, "There is growing evidence of the fact of obsession which lies at the basis of much insanity and can be cured. . . . The term 'obsession' is employed by psychic researchers to denote the abnormal influence of spirits on the living." [6] And Dr. Hereward Carrington writes in Modern Psychical Phenomena, "It is evident that spiritual 'obsession' is at least a possibility which modern science can no longer disregard while there are many striking facts in its support." [7] I have also been impressed by the wealth of evidence offered in Possession, Demoniacal and Other by Oesterreich. And what of the hospital in Brazil where, I am credibly informed by a physician, four hundred beds accommodate patients who are "possessed"?

3. Thirdly, we must admit the psychological phenomenon of multiple personality. In his famous study of Sally Beauchamp, Dr. Morton Prince[8] tells us he found several person-

[5] Proceedings of the American Society for Psychical Research, Vol. 3 (1909), p. 586.

[6] Quoted from Carl A. Wickland, Thirty Years Among the Dead (Spiritualist Press), p. 8.

[7] Quoted from Wickland, op. cit., p. 9.

[8] See Morton Prince, The Dissociation of a Personality (London: Longmans, Green).

alities acting within the same body, and, strangely enough, they were at loggerheads with one another. The original Miss Beauchamp hated spiders, but another personality taking charge of her body went and collected spiders, packed them in a box, and posted them to the original Sally who opened them. Says the narrative, "They nearly sent her into fits." If a personality can be controlled by "entities" as different as this, all within one body and mind, is it incomprehensible that a discarnate entity with evil intention, an evil spirit in fact, might possess a person?

4. The phenomena of Spiritualism make us ask similar questions. I have myself in my own study heard a "direct-voice medium" talk successively like a paper boy from the streets, an Anglican clergyman, and a cultured woman. Fraud excluded (and for me it was excluded), if entities can use the voice of a medium in this way, can we rule out possession by evil powers as impossible?

5. The evidence from missionary experience seems to me to be relevant and weighty. I read, in a magazine called *Christian Witness* (December, 1954), a story by a woman doctor of medicine, a missionary in China, in which she diagnosed one of her patients as being demon possessed. The patient was cured by casting out the demon by the power of Christ. I transcribe part of the treatment. The doctor speaks: "Now," I urged, "ask Jesus to cast out that evil spirit." Without any hesitancy the patient said, "*Ch'iu chu Yesu gan gwei.*" [9] Then the doctor urged the patient to pray, not only for the casting out of a demon, but that the Holy Spirit might be given "to

[9] "Gwei" according to Nevius is the term used in China by the common people to indicate the ghostly presence feared by all and given by every family some measure of propitiatory sacrifice.

130

occupy the empty place." The patient prayed thus, "Lord Jesus, please cleanse my heart and fill it with your Holy Spirit for the rest of my life." "From that moment," said the doctor, "she was well."

I am not dogmatic about all this. I have given what is, in my view, more convincing evidence in the book of which this one is but a footnote,[10] but I think missionary evidence, so sincere and so widespread, must be taken into consideration, and cannot easily be ruled out as nonsense, or ignorance of other explanations.

6. Consider also a story like this from an impeccable source.[11] Dr. Elwood Worcester was treating a certain young woman who presented symptoms of schizophrenia. One trying symptom persisted. Suddenly, while talking, the patient's head would drop, she would appear hardly conscious, and for hours afterward would remain depressed, weak, gloomy, and tearful. During this time her expression would change and become vacant and remote.

Dr. Worcester tells us that he himself has had very little psychic experience, but during the period he was treating this patient, he had a strange dream followed by a yet stranger experience. He fortunately reported both dream and experience to two members of his family immediately. On the morning of May 10, 1930, he was awakened by the consciousness of a presence in his bedroom. This "apparition" showed itself to be a Chinaman who came up from behind him and laid his cold, leathery cheek against his own. The doctor wrote, "Though I have absolutely no fear of such presences, there was

[10] Psychology, Religion and Healing, op. cit., pp. 94-95.
[11] Elwood Worcester in Making Life Better, (New York: Charles Scribner's Sons, 1933), pp. 50-53.

something sinister and evil about this apparition which made me shudder. When he had passed a foot or two before me, he turned, giving me a perfect view of his yellow face, his high brow, aquiline nose, white hair and burning, sunken eyes. He said, in a mocking, ironical manner, 'I beg your pardon.' "

The curious thing is that, unable to make progress with his patient, Dr. Worcester sought the aid of a medium whom he calls "a gentle, cultured psychic." He did not, of course, tell the medium anything of his dream and he writes as follows:

I did not, of course, give this lady any information in regard to my patient, nor even tell her that she was to meet anyone but me. In the course of our conversation the familiar phenomena occurred. The girl's head suddenly dropped, tears rained down her cheeks, she remained silent for several minutes, and when she lifted her head again all her gaiety and vivacity had disappeared and she was dull and apathetic.

Observing these changes, the medium asked me if I wished her to tell what she had observed and, receiving an affirmative reply, she said, "Just before this collapse took place, I saw an old man with leathery, yellow skin, like an Oriental, glide into the room with averted face and lay his hand upon the patient's head. His forehead was high, white hair hung over his brow, and he wore a white, Eastern head-dress. At the moment his hand rested on your patient's head she collapsed."

I asked, "What is our procedure?" and she replied, "I wish to pray silently first and to summon my allies. Then I wish you both to pray for her deliverance. Then we should offer our prayers together." This exercise occupied about fifteen minutes. After we had concluded our prayers, the psychic said, "This is all that is necessary. Two high and holy spirits came in response to our petition and I saw them take the obsessing personality by the hands and lead him far, far away, not to punish him but to educate and train him for his life in the spiritual world. He can never return."

This event took place in November, 1930, and that attack was the final one. I have kept in contact with this patient and saw her last about ten days ago. She told me then that she had regarded herself as well for more than a year and that she had not suffered the depressing, stupefying experience I have described since that day.

The immediate cessation of attacks which had lasted sixteen months is certainly striking. I know, of course, that a medium can often read the deep mind of another person and this one may have "seen" the Chinaman incident in the deep mind of the doctor. I know also that "Chinamen" seem too ready to haunt the séance room just as dead North American Indian doctors seem to be uncannily ready to come to our aid. We all get a little tired of "Blue Feather," and "Black Hawkeye," and "White Eagle," or, by way of variation, "Dr. Akobi Tabberwok."

Yet, for myself, I am left wondering why the doctor very much concerned with that particular patient had that particular postdream experience six months *before* the medium "saw" the Oriental, and although the medium's method contained powerful suggestion, I am left wondering at the sudden recovery of a patient who had been ill so long.

When we add together in our minds the effect of the six numbered paragraphs above, perhaps we, who as Christians believe presumably in the existence of angels, may have to make room in our thought for evil spirit-entities also. Jesus apparently believed in angels, and was comforted by their presence. (Matt. 4:11; 25:31; 26:53; Mark 1:13; Luke 22:43;

John 20:12.) It looks to me as if he believed in devils. Was he wrong in both these beliefs? Was he as wrong as all that?

The reader will wonder when I am going to discuss the case of Madge Davies. I felt, however, that no modern would entertain for a moment the idea that the diagnosis of demon possession might be correct unless I did all I could to prepare the ground. *Even now it is the last hypothesis to which I should myself be driven, and I only advance it as a possibility.*

Madge Davies was seventeen when I saw her first. She came a long distance from a country area which I will not name. Her mother accompanied her, and, consumed with shame and embarrassment, almost whispered the story to me while Madge waited in an adjoining room. The story was that while Madge appeared to be a normal, happy, healthy country girl, she appeared at times to undergo a metamorphosis which was terrifying in the extreme. She would go down on all fours and bark like a dog. She would lick a hand stretched out to her; if rebuked she would snarl, snap, and even attempt to bite. Normally of entirely clean habits, when she was in this condition she would urinate and defecate wherever she happened to be, using the positions assumed by a dog.

I had never seen any cases of this kind before, though I had read about them. I listened carefully and I interviewed Madge, but I felt that if ever a medically trained and experienced psychiatrist were needed, this was the time. Working in my clinic team at that time was a most able, thoroughly equipped, and efficient psychiatrist who was a deeply religious man, and who later became the head of an important mental hospital in Britain. I therefore explained the situation to him and he took over the case. He saw the patient repeatedly over a series of months, but on his own confession he could make no impression. He, of course, could consider methods not open to me such as stimulating the brain by a series of electric shocks called electro-convulsive-therapy (ECT) or even an operation of the brain, putting out of action its frontal lobes (prefrontal leucotomy), but he decided against both. Finally, we had to tell the girl and her mother that we had both done our best, but we did not feel we could usefully spend more time on her case. I had a letter from the parents thanking the doctor and myself for what we had tried to do, and telling us how grateful —but also how disappointed—they were. The patient herself, when her case was given up, had sobbed herself to sleep after a wild, incoherent storm of passion. She felt that all hope was gone and that this horrible, loathsome obsession would haunt her for the rest of her days.

It is most disturbing, of course, to let someone feel that nothing more can be done, and I could not get the girl out of my mind. One night I dreamed about her, and on waking I realized, with remorse, that though I professed to believe in prayer, I had never made her the object of our intercessions for the sick, nor had I focused on her in my own prayers. I wrote to the mother and promised that on the next Sunday evening the congregation at the City Temple, without my mentioning the girl's name or the details of her disability, would lift her up in earnest prayer to God.

In those days the old City Temple was packed with worshipers and an overflow congregation met in the hall below the church. Probably, therefore, well over two thousand people, if they put their thought and imagination to the task, prayed for Madge that evening.

A letter from Madge's mother spoke of an immediate improvement. Madge's spirits rose and symptoms diminished but we waited eagerly to see if the improvement lasted.

From that night in October, 1937, to the present time, Madge has not had a return of serious symptoms, and I am writing these words more than twenty years after the event, though of course I wrote careful notes at the time. She took up the career on which she had set her heart and she is perfectly well. More recently the chairman of the Methodist District in which Madge lived visited her home, met her parents, and interested himself in her case. He interviewed Madge herself and then wrote to me confirming what, after so long a time of freedom from symptoms, I think we can fairly call a cure. I met this district chairman again in December, 1961, and he confirmed this account.

I don't pretend to understand this case; I can't prove demoniacal possession, nor can I prove that prayer had anything to do with recovery. Did not Jesus himself say of one case, "There is no means of casting out this sort but prayer"? (Mark 9:29 N.E.B.) I have come to believe that while intercession for the sick is not always rewarded by the recovery of the patient, yet in some cases it appears to be the most important therapeutic factor.[12] Intercession, of course, does not mean telling God something he does not know or overcoming his reluctance to act. It is rather a co-operating with his willingness, as Dr. Fosdick once expressed it. There are so many situations in which God, as it were, waits for our willingness to co-operate with him, and prayer for the sick seems to me a willingness to lend our minds and feelings to God just as the surgeons, doctors, and nurses lend their hands to him, hands which

[12] I have given full details of such a case in *Psychology, Religion and Healing, op. cit.,* pp. 508 ff., and on pp. 117 ff. in this book.

obey trained minds. No one heals but God. All we can do is to lend him our powers in willing, trustful co-operation. If modern psychological theory is right, all minds are united at deep levels, and if the optimism, hope, faith, and love of two thousand people is strong enough, probably it can seep into, and alter the quality of, the deep mind of a patient. Distance is no barrier, nor is the unconscious state of the patient. And if the deep mind of the latter is changed from weakness, despair, and pessimism to strong hope, courage, and optimism, then bodily and mental disease have less chance of victory and evil entities might conceivably be driven out.

Strangely enough, while I was writing these words I had a letter from an intelligent correspondent who says,

I would like to relate a strange case of demon-possession I recently investigated. It was a woman who under the power of a dog-like demon acted as a dog. She would howl, bark, lick and behave exactly as a canine beast. Sometimes she would also throw herself to the ground and wriggle her body about in an abnormal manner, saying she was now a serpent. This is, however, not the first and only case. There have been others of a similar nature. A little girl who lives in Hadleigh, Suffolk, was likewise possessed of a dog-like demon. She would snap, snarl, and even bite anyone who approached her. A friend of mine (a very well-known evangelist) visited her and he commanded the demon to come out of her in Christ's name, and it did, in the presence of several witnesses. She is still in her right mind today.

If this groping demonology is in any sense sound, there is no place for alarm. The glory of Christ's resurrection to the members of the early church was not the assurance that they would

137

survive death. They believed that already.[13] They preached the Resurrection in nearly every sermon because they felt that evil powers had done their worst in putting Jesus to death, but that, having risen, he had conquered the demons and overcome triumphantly all that evil could do. The Resurrection is in some churches only referred to on Easter Day, and then sometimes it sounds merely like a happy ending to Good Friday's sad story. But it is relevant to every attack and seeming victory of evil. Christ has triumphed once and for all and can never know defeat. Christ, in the unseen, reigns, and Christ is available today. These are the tremendous affirmations of the Christian religion and they are the weapons with which the Christian fights.

If modern research in psychic science compels us to make room in our thinking for the possibility that in rare cases evil entities invade living people and produce disharmony of mind and body, such a discovery might turn out to be an advance indeed, if it made us explore more fully and use more faithfully and usefully the immense and largely untried therapeutic energies which are inherent in the Christian religion.

[13] John 11:24, where Martha says about the dead Lazarus, "I know that he shall rise again in the resurrection at the last day."

138

X

The Case of

BERT ABBOTT

BERT WAS A LIKEABLE LAD IN HIS THIRTIES, BUT HE PASSED through a most trying experience and I want to write about him so that others may escape the bitter disappointment and mental desolation which overwhelmed him.

When I first met him in a northern city he had been a cripple for eight years. Medical men said he would never walk again, and he himself had given up hope. He had been in a hospital for two-and-a-half years with one bad leg, and then, shortly after he had been told that nothing more could be done and he was discharged, he was knocked down by a car and the other leg was badly injured. When I saw him first he was using two crutches, but I never learned what the final medical diagnosis of his condition was.

Here are some words of his own as given to a reporter on an evening paper:

The doctors said I would never walk again and I was in constant pain. Then I was told about Pastor ——'s Mission. With the help of friends I went there. I had almost to be carried on to the platform. After Pastor —— had placed his hands on me and prayed, I knew that I was healed. It was the most wonderful happening in my life. I walked off the platform unaided and I have been able to walk without the help of anyone ever since.

Dramatically Bert threw away his crutches. The local papers on a certain evening—I still have the cutting—were full of his story and published his photograph. What they never did report is the grim fact that within three weeks Bert bought new crutches, felt the old pain, and resumed his former life of disablement, asking some puzzling questions which no one seemed able to answer. Bert was still a cripple when I last heard of him.

This sort of thing happens only too often.[1] A patient who sent me full details of his case, an educated man with degrees in science and philosophy, went to a "healing mission" in a northern city and sent me a letter containing the following:

I was the second person he treated. . . . I was not in the slightest degree emotionally moved. After enquiring the nature of my complaint, he laid his hand on my right temple and prayed fervently. I then felt what can only be described as a current of healing power pass from him to me. As a result, I could walk a few steps without limping and the tremor ceased. He then asked was I cured, and, on receiving my reply in the affirmative, asked me to repeat, "Thank you, Jesus." This, I am ashamed to say, I did. He then proclaimed my cure to the meeting. The effect, however, soon wore off. I estimate a period of about five minutes before the limp returned. The tremor, however, was absent, and I remained free from it even at breakfast next morning. I repeat, I was quite detached and had no emotional feelings whatever beyond curiosity. I cannot explain the temporary cure, but I have heard of similar cases, in one of which a patient suffering from diabetes was cured temporarily.

[1] See the letter printed on p. 62.

The temporary alleviation was due, in my opinion, to a brief and inadequate response to odic force.

While I was President of the Methodist Church, I visited in my official capacity every Methodist district in the country. One of these districts flouted the official direction of the Methodist Conference of 1952, which declared that Methodist premises must not be used for healing services to which the uninstructed general public is admitted. The official wording, sanctioned by the Conference, runs as follows:

The supreme aim of Healing Services should be the unity of the worshipper with God. The Conference directs that persons attending such services for the purpose of receiving the ministry of the laying on of hands should have been prepared in private by their ministers and have received the consent of their doctors. As far as possible, the officiant at Healing Services should know the doctor's diagnosis and understand the patient's condition. Such services would then signify the dedication of the patient in an act of surrender to God in loving trustfulness, whether recovery be attained or not. The end of the service would be the glory of God, rather than an attempt to use Him in order to get well.

In the district which had disregarded the Conference instruction—which, by the way, is still in force—I met many victims of healing missions and heard of many more. In one case the "healer" had told a housewife that if she had faith as big as a grain of mustard seed she would get up and do the housework. The poor soul did so, breaking thus the injunction of her physician. Within an hour, I was told, she fell dead from coronary thrombosis.

I append in furtherance of my plea that "healing services" to which unscreened members of the public are admitted for

141

treatment should not be held, the following cutting from a well-known newspaper:

"MIRACLE" WORKER AT ALBERT HALL

A young girl carried in the arms of a man. A crippled child led by his mother. A blind girl led by her sister. An old man hobbling along on sticks.

These were among the pathetic scenes at the Albert Hall yesterday afternoon when "The annual Elim Foursquare Gospel demonstration" was conducted by Pastor George Jeffreys, the founder of the movement.

Mr. Jeffreys believes in miracles, and at the close of a passionate address, in which he insisted that *unless one accepted the Virgin Birth there was nothing left of Christianity,*[2] he invited members of the audience who wished to be healed of some illness to stand up.

About 1,000 stood up. There followed a sad procession to the platform, so that he could "lay hands" on them and anoint them with oil. The crush was so great that Mr. Jeffreys had to appeal to those who had not reached the platform to return to their seats. It would probably have taken nearly two hours to anoint all who wanted to be healed.

Mr. Jeffreys' method was the same with each case. He put both hands on the head of the sufferer, and then murmured, "In the name of the Lord I anoint thee with oil." The only exception was the crippled child. He impulsively kissed him.

About four sufferers a minute were dealt with. They passed quickly across the platform in a queue and then back to the body of the hall. The blind girl had tears in her eyes as she was led, *still blind,* back to her seat. *The crippled child was still crippled. The young girl who had been carried to the platform was carried away*

[2] Italics mine. This idea is disproved by the fact that the Virgin Birth was never part of the missionary message of the church. Paul never mentioned it.

from it. No one anointed yesterday afternoon claimed at the time to be cured.

I cannot dismiss lightly words spoken to ministers by Paul Tillich, "Faith-healing as practiced by many groups is one of the worst abuses of religion today." Those of Professor John G. McKenzie are equally significant.[3] He says: "There is no subject on which I get less inclination to write than Spiritual Healing. In over forty years' experience I have never come across a case personally of either a physical or mental cure where a patient has been cured by any one of the various methods of spiritual healing."

It is because of this type of healing service in which all kinds of patients present themselves, in which the healer never even knows what is wrong and blindly adopts the same "treatment" for all, putting all the onus of "having faith" on the patient (who, for all the healer knows may be in urgent need of some more relevant treatment such as surgery, drugs, or diet) that I strongly approve of the direction given by the Methodist Conference. It surely must be realized that an emotional atmosphere is inevitable. No one can see a lot of sick people gathered together without feeling deeply moved. In some services of this kind this emotion is artificially increased by singing. I quote from a *British Weekly* account of a healing service:

No one who saw the cavalcade of sufferers will easily forget the pathetic sight. Before eight o'clock in the morning hundreds of sick and infirm folks crowded to the church. They came from all parts of England, and they came in strange fashion—a long procession of

[3] Both were quoted in *The British Weekly* of September 3, 1959.

motor-cars, bath chairs, spinal carriages, and similar conveyances—
and the pale faces of these lame, blind and broken people made a
moving spectacle. Dramatic incidents were numerous.

The writer adds, "In my investigations I have not found one
complete and instantaneous cure. The report that some blind
women had had their sight restored is quite untrue."

In Bradford in 1924, although the Bishop of Bradford laid
down that emotion was to be kept at a minimum and the
atmosphere within the parish church at Frizinghall was calm,
one read in the *Manchester Guardian* that "the whole church
was surrounded by excited crowds." Dr. Temple commented,
"That is exactly the kind of excitement from which our Lord
withdrew." In such an atmosphere symptoms often temporarily disappear and false hopes are given birth, which die a
death devastating indeed to the mind of the patient. Unless
the deep underlying cause of the disease is dealt with—and
the cause may, of course, be psychological—even if the symptom permanently disappears, the unconscious mind will express its continuing dis-ease in another symptom much harder
to cure.

I took a great interest in one woman healer and spent many
hours with her trying to understand. I arranged for her to
"treat" ten patients in my own home. Two are dead, the others
are much as they were. None got any discernible improvement.
She went to a city in another country, and I asked a friend of
mine, Dr. A, to report. He wrote, "No case of actual healing
where the person treated was known to be suffering from a
specific disease has been known here." The healer moved to
yet another country where I have a friend who wrote: "The
cases I have followed up have *all* had pathetic endings."

Another correspondent who attended her "healing services" wrote, 'Not one could I trace who could definitely say they were healed of their diseases." Yet another friend wrote of a patient of this healer: "The patient *thought* she was cured but is now as bad as ever. Yet the healer made many claims of 'cures.'"

I cannot help being glad to find that the late Dr. Cyril Garbett, formerly Archbishop of York, agreed with my own opinions about healing services. Addressing Convocation he said:

Without prayer and preparation, the laying on of hands and anointing might come dangerously near magic. . . .

If careful preparation of the individual sick person is necessary for healing, it follows that this is a grave objection to public missions of healing, where preparation of individuals is impossible and where hands are laid indiscriminately upon all who come to them. . . . I am speaking of the sensational and much advertised missions held sometimes by American evangelists, but occasionally in our own Church. I believe these do great harm by their hysterical and emotional atmosphere and by making unjustifiable claims of cures.

About twenty-five years ago some of these missions were conducted by a well-known lay healer, now dead. A small committee of doctors and clergymen of which I was chairman, was asked by Archbishop Davidson to investigate the sensational claims made of numerous cures at them. Deliberately we postponed doing this until over a year had passed since the missions were held. After most careful inquiries, we found no evidence whatever to support the claims or to lead us to believe that there had been, as the result of the mission, any cures of organic disease or any lasting cures of functional disorders.

The Archbishop also said that when he was Bishop of South-wark there was a mission of healing in a large chapel not far from his house. For the first fortnight it was thronged, and an excited congregation saw the lame walk and the paralytic cured. The neighboring clergy were so impressed that they asked him to allow them to have a public mission of healing under the auspices of the Church. He refused. The Archbishop then added these significant words:

It would have proved unnecessary, for in the third week the mission of healing had to be abandoned on account of the return to it of so many who had gone away healed in the first week, and come back to protest indignantly that now they were worse rather than better.

I have tried to write all this in charity and in good will, and only hope that we can save would-be patients from those debacles and disappointments which have followed public healing missions.

Dr. Louis Rose of St. Bartholomew's Hospital attempted to check one hundred cases of healing by paranormal methods. *The Times* of December 3, 1954, reported as follows:

A psychiatrist on the staff of St. Bartholomew's Hospital, London, describes in the current issue of the *British Medical Journal* his investigation of nearly 100 examples of healing by what he calls "paranormal" methods. He concludes that no single case revealed conclusively that the healer's intervention alone resulted in improvement or cure of a measurable organic disability.

Some of the patients were treated by one healer and the investigator attended demonstrations to gain information about the nature of the work and its results. He wrote to as many patients as possible and tried to get permission for medical records to be made available. In over half the cases it was not possible to obtain such records or other independent information, so that claims made remain unconfirmed.

In three instances a change "rare but not unknown in orthodox medical experience" took place in the organic state of the patient soon after treatment by the healer. In four cases there was improvement when healing was received concurrently with orthodox medical treatment.

Power "Not Established"

It is concluded that the healer investigated "may have some power to influence the progress of disease, although this has not been established during the present survey." A plea is made for more detailed inquiry into a wide field of paranormal diagnosis and treatment.

"Clinical psychiatrists," states the present report, "employing suggestion as a specific therapeutic technique, continue to achieve healing results at least as encouraging as those met with in this series."

All this may seem disturbing to read and I know what a serious thing it is to appear to stand between a patient and any hope of healing. I only want to save him from the mental despair I have witnessed so often.

I am quite sure there are some cases which Christ himself could not have cured, making new limbs to grow instantaneously, for instance, or giving sight to a man whose eyes had been removed. Jesus Christ had more in common with a modern surgeon than a modern "faith healer," for he knew what was wrong and altered his technique accordingly and did not suppose that religion offered healing in every possible case.

147

If the church gave its assent to the demand for healing missions it would lose in a night what some of us have worked for for forty years, namely co-operation with the medical profession. At last this co-operation has been sanctioned, as the following statement shows. It is so important that I quote from a special Supplement to the *British Medical Journal* of November, 1947:[4]

The Council of the B.M.A. is of opinion that there is no ethical reason to prevent medical practitioners from co-operating with clergy in all cases, and more especially those in which the doctor in charge of the patient thinks that religious ministrations will conduce to health and peace of mind or lead to recovery. Such co-operation is often necessary and desirable, and would help to prevent abuses which have arisen through the activities of irresponsible and unqualified persons. Among other reasons the Churches' Council of Healing exists to safeguard the interests of those people who might become the victims of so-called faith healers. Much harm has been done to individuals by unreasonable appeals to the emotions and by mass hysteria. . . .

We welcome opportunities for discussion and co-operation in the future between qualified medical practitioners and all who have a concern for the religious needs of their patients.

What can be done in this field I have already stated. (See pp. 23-24), but do let us guard against claims for religion which Jesus would never have made. One of the saddest true stories came to me from the relative of a little boy aged nine with a clubfoot who was taken to a "healer" and promised that he would be healed, and that on the way home his parents

[4] The full statement I have printed in *Psychology, Religion and Healing, op. cit.*, pp. 229-31.

would buy him a pair of football shoes so that he could play like other boys. The healer duly laid hands on his head but nothing happened to his feet. Probably a lifelong wound developed in his mind, and his bitterness and disappointment hardly bear thinking about. Not only the healer but "Jesus," too, was put into the category of fakes and frauds.

I hope the time will come when every church or group of churches will have its healing ministry, such as we had and still have at the City Temple, whose Psychological Clinic now has the help of four ministers and twelve medically qualified psychologists and where no one who is not a minister or a doctor comes into contact with a patient, but where there is first the quiet interview between a qualified minister and the patient. The minister quickly learns what the patient needs; and if it is within his competence to help, he will readily do so. Behind him, so to speak, he has prayer circles and fellowship groups which again and again have proved their worth in getting a sick person well. But the minister may suspect that a thorough medical overhaul is indicated. He has both men and women physicians ready to help him there, and with the patient's permission they report back to him. A discussion may then show that technical, psychiatric skill is needed. This too is available. Thus the energies released by religion, medicine, and psychology can all be focused on the patient's need. Finally, should this be indicated, there is a loving community—which ought to be another name for the church—into which the wounded spirit can be received until his integration is effected. Then he can be a part of that community and help others to find integration, serenity, and comfort. Even then all cannot be healed, for this may not yet be within any human competence. In that case the patient is given the maximum help to

149

live with his disability. He is saved from the shock of false hopes and from making false deductions about God and about himself and about his faith or lack of it when cure is not yet reached. All the terrible dangers of healing missions are avoided, and not one of its apparent advantages is missed. And the church of Christ can live up to an old adage, "To cure sometimes, to alleviate often, to comfort always."

XI

The Case of

DR. MARY FAWCETT

DURING A PERIOD OF OVER FORTY-FIVE YEARS IN THE CHRISTIAN ministry—over forty of them years in which I have taken a special interest in psychological problems and in healing—I do not think I have ever met quite so strange a case as the one I have permission to describe in this chapter, though I have read of such cases in the monumental works of Havelock Ellis and others. This narrative has been read by Dr. Fawcett and approved as correct, though neither of us can even now understand all the factors which have operated to bring about a transforming change in a wounded spirit. We both believe that a Christian experience has been the most important therapeutic factor. If only such an experience could, so to speak, be engineered and repeated so that others might come through a dismal valley as Dr. Fawcett did, it would be splendid. But that is just what no one can arrange.

However, to start at the beginning, Mary Fawcett discovered in early days that she was a congenital homosexual. As the reader probably knows, homosexuals are of two types, those who are born that way and those who acquire it, usually through the experience of being sexually assaulted very early in life by a member of the same sex. Mary belonged to the former category; she was born that way. As sexuality developed at puberty she became conscious that, unlike other girls, she was not attracted to boys but to girls. She loved fondling and petting them without realizing why.

Later on she had what she describes as two "affairs" with girls. Fortunately, though she practiced masturbation on them both, she did not deflect their sex life from its heterosexuality and now both girls are happily married. Mary studied medicine and qualified as a doctor, only to find a fierce desire raging within her to examine sexually girl patients and—a temptation which she usually withstood—to stimulate them by sexual manipulation.

About this time she developed another passionate and extraordinary desire: namely, to change her sex and become a man. This desire, which most people would have immediately dismissed as impossible and absurd, possessed her mind day and night, and when she read the strange story of how Robert Cowell, a man, became Roberta, a woman, the impossible seemed to become possible. The story of Roberta has been written by herself and published by William Heinemann Ltd., with a Preface by Canon Millbourn of Bristol Cathedral. With the publisher's written permission I feel free to quote from the dust cover as follows:

Robert Cowell grew up like most other English boys. He was a surgeon's son, was given a conventional education and was a rugger wing three-quarter at school. In his curiosity to find out how things worked he took bits of machinery to pieces and he hoped to fly an aeroplane and drive a racing car when he was old enough.

Unlike most boys, he realised his ambitions. When he was seventeen he joined the R.A.F., got his "Wings," and became the youngest pilot in the Service. His persistent airsickness, however, was not according to his plan, and he was invalided out as unsuitable for flying duties. When the war came he joined the Army and, after reaching the rank of captain, succeeded in transferring back to the R.A.F. He flew as a Spitfire pilot over France and Germany until he was shot down east of the Rhine and finished the war in a prison camp.

Cowell had driven racing cars before the war and when he was demobilised he began driving again, in contests with such famous racing drivers as Raymond Mays and Prince Bira. From engineering he turned to dress-designing and then, in an effort to resolve the doubts and increasing unhappiness which he realised existed in his mind, he went first to a psychiatrist, later to a physician. They agreed that latent feminine characteristics, both physical and psychological, were developing in him. Cowell was faced with the choice of remaining male and becoming increasingly feminine in mind and body—or of becoming a woman. He chose the latter course and, some months after being re-registered, on a doctor's authority, as a woman, modern plastic surgery was called upon to aid the change begun by nature. After a series of operations and slow metamorphosis, psychological as well as physical, Robert Cowell emerged as Roberta Cowell, a woman.

Simply told and very moving, this is the story of a brave man, a war hero who had been married and was the father of two children, who had the courage to follow the strange destiny reserved for him by nature and who emerged, as an equally brave woman, to meet and surmount difficulties such as few human beings have ever been called upon to face.

The book is illustrated at the beginning (pp. 12-13, 60-61) with photographs of the hero as a man, and at the end (pp. 124, 133) with photographs of a pretty, blonde girl doing her shopping and cooking. They are one and the same person. Male sexuality was successfully changed to female.

This story set Dr. Mary thinking harder than ever, and longing even more intensely to become a man. So she wrote to Roberta who told her the name of the surgeon who had assisted her to change her sex and become a woman. It should be noted that Robert also had some psychoanalysis from a Freudian analyst and discovered, to use his own words, "that my unconscious mind was predominantly female" (p. 71). "Freed from repressions," he said, "I was psychologically a woman." This was a devastating discovery and made the patient very unhappy.

The surgeon concerned, whose name I do not even know, examined Dr. Mary, and told her that he promised nothing except that her periods would probably stop; but after due preparation it is alleged that he made an incision over the region of the right ovary, and inserted a tube containing male hormone. The substance of the tube was gradually absorbed, and presumably the hormones were received into the bloodstream. This insertion of a tube took place four times.

Mary hoped that her breasts would shrink and give her chest a male appearance; that the clitoris would enlarge to become a male penis; that testicles would develop, the vagina close, and the uterus atrophy. Presumably she more than merely hoped, since she was in correspondence with a living person in whom sex changes had taken place in the opposite direction, and she was under the same doctor who had achieved in Robert Cowell—and, I am told, in other people also—a complete and successful change of sex.

Such changes of sex, though most readers will be unaware of the fact, are not so very uncommon. In 1952 (September 12) the press reported that a Scottish doctor, aged forty, pre-

viously a woman, had, after male hormone treatment, become
a man. He later married.

Later in the same year, the press reported the story of an
American man, George Jorgensen, aged twenty-four, who had
hormone treatment in Copenhagen. With surgical treatment
in addition, this U.S. soldier got permission from Washington
to have a new passport made out in the name of Christine
Jorgensen. She wrote home to her parents and said, "Nature
made a mistake which I have had corrected and now I am your
daughter." She subsequently made a living by appearing in
cabarets, with presumably considerable sex appeal.

The Danish painter Einar Wegener, although happily married at twenty, found at forty that slow changes were taking
place within him. Rudimentary ovaries were found, ovarian
tissue from a healthy young woman of twenty-six was surgically
inserted, hormone treatment being then unknown, and he became a woman. Danish authorities annulled his marriage and
issued a new passport in the name of Lili Elbe. The wife
married a mutual friend; and a French painter, who had been
an old friend of Einar and his wife for many years, fell in love
with Lili.[1]

It is very rare for men to change their sex and become
women, but it is not extremely uncommon for women to become men. But alas, to Mary's disappointment, the metamorphosis did not take place. Mary put on two stones in
weight, her breasts developed rather than shrank. Her waist
increased, black hair appeared on her chest, her thighs, and her

---

[1] I owe these facts to *Roberta Cowell's Story* by herself (London: William
Heinemann Ltd., 1954), pp. 122 ff. Many other illustrations are provided, and
permission to quote has been given.

legs, and, most alarmingly, her voice deepened until her friends noticed it and asked awkward questions.

Then she wrote to me. She explained that she was a truly religious person, a communicant of the Church of England, but that she had come to worship with us at the City Temple one evening and felt attracted to our way of worship. She wrote as follows:

What you said in the sermon greatly impressed me, and as a result I feel that you would be able to help me.

It is very difficult to write down my dilemma, but may it be sufficient to say that because of my particular make-up, another way of life is both attractive and possible. I've prayed about things but I honestly find it most difficult to know which course to follow.

So many people, if I were to try to discuss my position, would be both prejudiced and unsympathetic.

On reading through my letter I seem to have failed to stress the depth of my problem, it is nothing superficial I can assure you.

I should therefore, be most grateful if you would deign to spare me some of your very valuable time so that this matter might be thoroughly thrashed out.

Yours very sincerely,

Of course I saw her and we talked together for over an hour. She explained that she was an only child and had always wanted to be a boy. In her childhood she had been a real tomboy and had played with trains and guns. As she grew up she felt "a crush on girls" and then felt sexually attracted to them and wanted to embrace them intimately. She longed, all through her student life, to be a man, and took the steps I have narrated to try to become one.

156

The first thing I had to do was to remove from her mind the burden of guilt which she laid bare. "Whether congenital or acquired, homosexuality is not in itself a mark of mental deficiency or moral degradation." [2] She had been born that way and could not help being a homosexual, though she realized that it was very wrong to corrupt others. But there was no sin about her *feelings*. People can be born with psychological as well as with physical abnormalities. She realized, however, that she must be most careful not to practice any homosexual acts with young girls, lest she deflect their sexuality into homosexual channels and possibly rob them of happy and contented marriage. This she saw clearly. We felt that her abnormality, properly controlled, could even be an asset. She might readily, as a doctor, be consulted by homosexuals and she could understand them with a sympathy withheld from most.

The next thing I felt I must advise her about was that she should cease all treatment of the kind described above, have no more injections of male hormone, and accept her femininity and stop even thinking how much better life would be if she could change her sex. It was clear from her full figure that it would take years for her to achieve as complete a change of sex as Robert Cowell had achieved, and I gave my opinion that the whole idea should be given up.

Dr. Mary is a very devout person. She said that it was her moral uncertainty which had made her come to me, and I tried to show her that as her religious experience deepened and she accepted her womanhood and used it (together with a probably ineradicable *trend* toward homosexuality) in the

[2] Havelock Ellis, *The Psychology of Sex*, I, 198.

service of God, via her patients, her life would become integrated, serene, and happy.

She wrote (June 18, 1960):

The very fact that I was able to unburden myself to you helped tremendously. It is not going to be easy adopting the position which you advocated, for it has been so contrary to my thinking and behaviour for so long. However, reviewing one's position and facing up to it is a terrific step forward.

Inevitably there must be much searing of soul and body, before the cave is reached, and one is both ready and willing to hear the "still, small voice."

Gratefully Yours,

The reader can imagine my delight at learning, from a further letter dated October 4, 1961, that Dr. Mary has been promoted; that her religious life has carried her to the place of serenity which I prophesied; that she lives alone but quite contentedly, hardly ever feeling now the physical longing to have young, attractive girls near her. Then she added this: "I feel very much now a womanly woman and hope that Mr. Right may appear on the scene if that is to be."

This is a tremendous assertion for a one-time sufferer from innate homosexuality to make, and it was my turn to request an interview. When I saw her again I was delighted with all that had happened. The patient had lost a little weight, but appeared to be mentally and physically a completely normal and happy woman. She told me that spiritually she was exercising a strict discipline on herself, and that she felt entirely master of the sexual situation. For her even to contemplate marriage makes one feel that her homosexuality is cured and that she could be a happy wife and mother.

Does it mean that self-discipline, patience, the acceptance of disability as a spiritual challenge, and a determination to use abnormality to help others, can, with a little belief and encouragement from another who does not scorn or condemn, add up in some cases to a mastery which could be labeled "cure" or at least victory over a tendency which, if yielded to, would have led into an abyss of misery for herself and others? Or did our interview help Dr. Mary—perhaps wrongly supposed to be an innate homosexual—to pass out of a phase of arrested sexual development? We all pass through a temporary phase of homosexuality as we develop—for example, when the schoolgirl has a *grande passion* for a teacher, or the schoolboy "hero worships" a master—and Dr. Mary's may have been halted for some reason. No one can be dogmatic about this, but the case of the now radiant and happy Dr. Mary Fawcett, a vital Christian if ever there was one, leads me along avenues of hope.

I think the narration of this case may encourage and help the many among us who are homosexuals. I can relate it the more happily because I did nothing.[3] Dr. Fawcett had no psychological treatment, not even suggestion, from me or from anyone else. Only three people in the world know the details of her case: herself, her surgeon, and myself. All I tried to do was to banish her sense of guilt, persuade her to accept her femininity, encourage her to control her abnormal trend, and, as it were, offer it to God for his use through her work. Her

[3] This is the only sentence in this account with which Dr. Mary does not agree. She writes (November 18, 1961): "I feel very humbled as I think over events and cannot agree that you did nothing. Your understanding was tremendous. I was most conscious and still am of your prayers and fellowship." All the same, her own faith and courage were the decisive factors.

159

own faith, courage, and determination did the rest. No doubt a homosexual tendency still lurks in her deep mind, but we nearly all harbor *tendencies* to perversion. Sadism, masochism, and other perversions show themselves in many "normal" people I have met. But there is all the difference in the world between a perversion and a tendency to a perversion. Dr. Fawcett's case at any rate points a way in which we can rob perversion of much of its power over us, and possibly—as in her case—allow the patient to live a happy, contented, serene, and useful life.

XII

The Case of

ALISTAIR DALTON

ONE SUNDAY EVENING I WAS JUST STARTING FROM MY HOME TO take the service at the City Temple when the telephone rang in the hall. I answered it to hear the tearful voice of a young mother whom I had known since her girlhood. Her little son Alistair, aged seven, was so ill with poliomyelitis that the doctor, who had just left the house, had expressed the terrifying opinion that "the boy would be dead before morning." "So," said his mother, "in desperation I turn to you. Do you think the people at the City Temple will pray for my little boy? His little sister, aged two, has got it also, though she is not so ill, and a young girl who helps me in the house has developed it. We are overwhelmed with sorrow, especially for Alistair, who appears to be dying."

What could I do but promise that that very evening we would concentrate at seven o'clock on Alistair? I asked the congregation not to think they were telling God something he didn't know, not to imagine that they were pleading with him, and, as it were, trying to make him come to the boy's help, nor to think of God as passively sympathizing and yet unable to help. I asked them to think of Christ standing by Alistair's little bed and laying his hands on the boy in healing power. I

161

asked them to believe that, as the doctors and nurses lent God their skill, we could lend him our love and caring; that just as a nurse, in certain cases, could rig up an oxygen tent to provide conditions in which God's healing power had more chance, so we could surround the deep mind of the boy with courage, hope, optimism, and the will to be well. Nurses could make his breathing easier. We could, as it were, surround his soul with the spiritual oxygen of our faith. Nearly two thousand people, that night—for I am sure that number were present and *interested*—became members of a healing team, with the family, the doctors, and the nurse. We were not overcoming God's reluctance but co-operating with his willingness. We imaginatively watched Christ standing in that bedroom, lovingly ministering to Alistair. Again and again I said to the people, "Don't let your mind wander. Watch and pray. Believe in recovery. In the atmosphere of our belief, Christ can more perfectly do his mighty work."

As soon as I got home I rang up the young mother. With what delight I heard her joyful voice, "Dr. Weatherhead, he is sitting up playing with his toys." Here is the letter she wrote a few days later in August, 1954.

Dear Dr. Weatherhead,

I feel I must write and thank you so very much for praying for Alistair in your church last Sunday and to tell you of the wonderful thing that happened. You prayed for him in your service at 7 p.m. All that day he was very ill and feverish and at 6:30 his temperature was 103 and over. At 7:30 he said, suddenly, "Mummy, I feel better now and can I have some supper?" His temperature dropped three degrees in that time. This fever had been due to a flare-up in his tonsils following the polio, but nothing to do with it. Today the orthopedic specialist has seen his legs and tells us that in time he will be able to walk and run again, but cannot guarantee that he will be left without any disability. It is going to be a long time ahead of him, but it is wonderful that there is every hope of such a good recovery.

May I ask you now to pray again for him, and in your own prayers for our other three children—also for me to increase my faith? I feel quite certain that prayer has helped and is helping Alistair.

Of course we had not forgotten the little sister. The letter added that she was out of danger and had escaped all paralysis. The young girl, aged seventeen, who helped in the house had had to go to the hospital and have the help of an iron lung. So I asked our six prayer circles, who daily lift up in intercession those whose names have been sent to them, if they would remember Alistair, his little sister, and Jenny the house help. We also remembered them all in prayer on successive Sunday evenings at seven o'clock.

Imagine how happy I felt then to receive the following letter from the young mother, herself once a patient in my psychological clinic in Leeds. This letter is dated October, 1954.

Dear Dr. Weatherhead,

I am quite convinced that your prayers brought our children through those anxious weeks. Alistair has even surprised the doctors. Firstly by learning to walk again more quickly than they expected, and secondly by the improvement in the strength of his muscles. . . . Caroline is now quite well again and has regained weight, appetite and colour during the last few days. Alistair was quite convinced that his recovery was a direct answer to prayer. Yesterday he went to church with us for the first time since his illness to say "Thank you" to God for making him better. This experience, I feel, will

surely remain with him all his life and make a lasting basis for
his own faith in prayer. Jenny is very much better. She is out of
the iron lung altogether, and though some groups of muscles are
weakened, they say she will also in time make a full recovery.

But from this happy story we must turn to some fearless and
grim conclusions.

The first is that it would be an inaccurate and foolish conclusion to suppose that prayer is a cure for polio. Alistair and
his little sister Caroline and Jenny were not cured, and Alistair
and Jenny may bear the consequences of the disease all their
lives even though Caroline appears to be unhandicapped. They
were apparently better than they would otherwise have been.
But God, if I may so state my own view, is not likely to allow
prayer to be a shortcut to save mankind the trouble of research,
of finding out what causes polio, and how, not only to cure it,
but prevent it altogether. I would rely much more on antipolio
vaccine than on prayer to guard our children from this foul
disease, and I hold that this is a *religious* point of view, just as,
if fire broke out in the study where I am writing these words,
I should throw on water and summon the fire brigade. I should
not fall on my knees and pray God to put out the fire. That
would certainly not be "loving God with all my mind," which
Jesus called the first commandment.

It is no disparagement of religion to remember that prayer
is not a cure-all. Certainly no argument for idleness and sloth
can be drawn from its operation, and while it is never without
value, it is often without therapeutic value. It is often not the
relevant way of co-operating with God in all situations that
arise. If the reader is shocked and thinks I am disparaging the
power of prayer, I will only ask him honestly to answer a ques-

tion my beloved teacher, Dr. W. R. Maltby, used to pose: "If you fell into the river and were drowning, would you rather see on the bank near you a burglar who could swim or a bishop who couldn't?" Clearly God could make better use of a swimming burglar than a sinking bishop.

Some things are clearly impossible of achievement, even by the most devout prayer. Who would pray that sight might be recovered in the case of a blind man, both of whose eyes had been removed? Who would pray that a woman might have a child if the organs of generation had been removed; or, to take the argument to its logical conclusion, who would pray that a man's life might be restored after his head had been blown off and had rolled down a bank into a river and been devoured by fish? Yet, *unknown to us*, many ill people for whom we pray are in situations which, did we but know it, would have to be placed in the same category. The God-designed machinery for recovery of function is missing or destroyed. We are to go on praying, but we are not to lose faith when prayer is not answered in the way we wish. All things are *not* possible to him that believeth if he believes in magic. I believe in miracles. They illustrate the impingement on to our plane of energies which are normal on a higher, super-natural plane. But I do not believe in magic, for that implies not the supernatural but the contranatural. And *that* implies a madhouse of a universe where nothing could confidently be learned about nature: in fact not a *universe* at all, for its unity would be destroyed.

I feel that I must be very honest in commenting on the case of Alistair Dalton. For over twenty-four years at the City Temple, and for eleven years before that in Leeds, whenever I led Sunday evening worship we offered intercession for the sick, mentioning, when we had permission, their names. Very rarely indeed, I should think in less than 5 per cent of cases, did we find our prayers followed by any marked improvement in the patient, and even then, of course, it was open to any critic to say of the patient, "He would have recovered in any case," and nothing we could say could ever prove that prayer was the decisive factor, although in some cases it seemed the most likely therapeutic factor.[1]

What frequently did happen, however, was that the patient reacted to his illness in quite a different way. In some cases the patient got no better physically but even said, "I felt that the illness *didn't matter any more.*"

One of our City Temple members, a university graduate in science, asked me in April, 1960, if I would ask the congregation to pray for his mother in Cornwall who was suffering from inoperable cancer. We concentrated our minds and hearts on her at seven o'clock one Sunday evening. Here is part of a letter her son wrote to me:

During Sunday, upon her return home, she was in some pain and very drowsy. She found it difficult to collect her thoughts. At seven p.m. she was sleeping, but on waking a little later, said, "I feel much better and that I have not a worry in the world. I had never realised how comfortable my bed was." We all saw such a big difference in her—it was an experience I shall never forget. Also the foul discharge which had been taking place, dwindled and almost stopped during the night. When I left Cornwall to return to London yesterday afternoon, Mother was in fine spirits, very cheerful and at peace with the world.

[1] I think a fair illustration of this is "The Case of David Hughes," described with full medical details and the reports of the doctors concerned in Appendix 3 of my book, *Psychology, Religion and Healing, op. cit.,* pp. 508 ff.

I believe now that prayer is the only help and wonder if it would be possible for her to be thought of again at the City Temple on Sunday next.

But before "Sunday next" came she was free from the diseased body, having slipped away happily knowing that the illness "didn't matter any more."

Let me set down here one very interesting discovery. Over a period of forty years, we have found in the course of offering public prayer for the sick that though prayer for adults is frequently disappointing, prayer for little children is far more frequently followed by recovery.

One must not be blind to the fact that children, in any case, recover from anything more quickly than adults. But I think there may well be a further factor. The mind of an adult is "made up," if the phrase can be allowed, as to what is possible and what is impossible. To be frank, I think if two or three able physicians assured me that my wife could not possibly recover from some illness, and if they convincingly explained why, I should find it very difficult to believe that the prayers of a congregation could be a powerful enough thera-peutic factor to prove them wrong. One of my dearest friends, at the height of his powers, when his preaching was probably influencing more people for God than any other voice in the country, was stricken with progressive muscular atrophy from which, I am told, no one has ever recovered. Every known treatment in Britain, on the Continent, and in America was tried, and literally hundreds of people, singly or in groups, prayed sincerely for him for over a year. Extraorthodox treat-ments were tried also. The disease attacked his vocal cords first, and the most powerful voice for Christ in Britain was

167

silenced. Then the use of his legs went. Then he died, without once losing his radiant, triumphant faith in God and in the value and importance of prayer. We must go on praying, of course. But we must not expect that God will necessarily fulfill our ideas of what he ought to do, based on what we should do if we had the power.

In the case of children, however, there seems far less resistance. Is it that they have not made up their minds as to what is and is not possible? Do young children, indeed, ever weigh up the matter at all? Are their deep minds far more easily influenced by the positive ideas of health and recovery released by the minds of people who are faithfully praying? Does the hope and optimism of a congregation invade their minds at an unconscious level, and effect enough difference to bring down the swinging balance on the side of recovery?

It is worth glancing for a moment at the nature of that mind, for one of the inquiries the church must patiently pursue is that into the laws of intercession. Our trouble now is that we pray for A and he recovers. We pray for B and he dies, and we so rarely understand why in either case.

It can now be assumed, I think, that at a deep level all human minds are united. If some unimaginable chemical change altered from its center the composition of the earth, then all the continents would show the change, however separated by sea they may be at the surface of the globe. "No man is an island entire in itself," said John Donne. Is it possible that minds, separated at the surface by bodies and called individuals, are, at some deep center, one; and can individuals be affected by forces released by prayer at that center?

By a study of birds, we get a glimpse of a unity of mind

168

combined with a separation of individuals who share that mind. Pigeons wheeling in a city square seem to be responding to a common mind. It appears that an impulse that strikes one pigeon strikes all together. Hence, without specific instruction from one to another, they wheel without bumping into each other and all apparently decide at the same instant when and where to turn and when and where to settle again. I remember that it was found that, in the north of England, blue tits started attacking milk bottles and piercing the caps to get at the milk. In an incredibly short time the same phenomenon was noted in the south. Was it telepathy or a kind of pooled "mind" to which all the species had access? Edmund Selous in *Thought Transference or What in Birds?* and Whately Carington in *Telepathy* long ago suggested this. The latter thinks that spiders have a subconscious pool of "spider knowledge," a kind of "pooled mind made up of the wisdom of its ancestors from which it can draw." [2] Eugene Marais in *The Soul of the White Ant* makes it clear that the colony, not the individual ant, is the psychical unit. "The individual is reduced to little more than a specialised cell endowed with automobility."

No authority in this field, I imagine, can be more decisive than that of Sir Alistair Hardy, professor of zoology in the University of Oxford. He writes[3] that, if an animal changed its habits to get food more easily, the changed pattern of activity might be passed on by telepathy. He says,

[2] Whately Carington, *Telepathy* (3rd ed.; London: Methuen, 1946), p. 160.
[3] "Telepathy and Evolutionary Theory" (*Proceedings of the Society for Psychical Research*, Vol. 35, No. 658 [June 1950]).

If a bird usually fed on insects off the surface of the bark of trees and then a few individuals found that they could get a good supply of insects by probing under the bark, they would be copied. If the plan proved beneficial, a wave of change in the behaviour plan might spread, not by copying but perhaps by a telepathic-like influence spreading from the individuals who made the discovery.

I quote this to show that reliable scientists are familiar with the idea that separation of body does not necessarily mean separation of mind. Professor Price, professor of logic at Oxford University, in a broadcast talk subsequently published in *The Listener*,[4] said, "It is nonsense to suppose that minds are spatially separate entities. . . . Minds are not objects in space. . . . We must suppose that on the unconscious level there are no sharp boundaries between one mind and another." Dr. Raynor Johnson in his book *The Imprisoned Splendour* gives enough evidence to convince anyone of the fact of telepathy between human beings.[5]

If this is so, it seems more credible to believe that if two thousand people in the City Temple were concentrating their minds on little Alistair Dalton, and if minds interpenetrate one another, their positive thoughts of recovery, health, buoyancy, and optimism might, if one may put it thus, alter the color of the patient's mind from the gloomy dull brown of illness to the rosy pink of expectancy, and this change might so strengthen and increase the forces already leagued against the germ invasion of poliomyelitis as to help win the battle against that disease.

At once the reader will offer a criticism. He will say that such

[4] February 13, 1947, pp. 277-88.
[5] (London: Hodder and Stoughton, 1953), pp. 107-26.

an explanation reduces intercession to "mere telepathy." He will ask where religion and God come in.

In reply two things must be said.

1. God is not ruled out of a process because we begin to understand it. What if the mechanism called telepathy is one of the mechanisms God uses when he seeks to answer our prayers? There are always some who think that God is the more manifested in that which is the less understood. If they are allowed to believe that God made mankind from dust by a word of command they are happy. When the word "evolution" is mentioned they feel that God is being excluded. But evolution, if true, only describes a method which God used, and telepathy may be a method God uses when we pray for the sick.

2. But I wish to put forward a thought which I have never yet seen expressed. If Christ really was an incarnation of God —and this I believe to be true—then he has added his truly human unconscious mind to the mind pool from which we all stem and to which we all have access. The whole human race has been incredibly enriched by what we call the Incarnation. God became man with not only a man's body but a man's mind. To the foul morass which Freud and others have shown human unconsciousness to be, has been added this "fountain of sweet water in the sea." Figures of speech fail us, but now our deep minds are in vital touch with his. So, although it may sound merely imaginative to ask a congregation to pray for a sick child and *imagine* Christ standing by the bed and laying his hands on the child, in reality their communion is not only true, but much deeper and interpenetrative than the imaginative picture suggests. And Christ's giving of himself has never been withdrawn. Even in the unseen, he is still

human, and still the friend of us all and the Savior of the race.[6]

What he *can,* or *could* possibly do, in various cases of illness, is not for man to decide. What he *does* do we must slowly learn. Like everything else in the universe, intercession also has its laws. But it seems reasonable to suppose that if God can use the words of a preacher to convert a soul, he can use the thoughts of a congregation to heal a body where the mind that uses that body is not walled up against him.

In conclusion, whatever is said or written about intercession for the sick, about its value or how it "works," people who love God and their sick loved ones will always pray for them. The heart of prayer is communion with God for its own sake, not for the sake of what we can get out of it for ourselves and our friends.

And let us remember that pray-ers, people who pray, are never unanswered, whatever may happen to their prayers. Let me put it directly to the reader: You have only to think of your own child clamoring for something from you. However silly it was, however impossible, however ridiculous, you would not, in stony indifference, avert your face and look the other way. Indeed, would it not be true to say that the more impossible or unwise the request from your child, the more you would gather him into your arms, love him, and comfort him; make up for the disappointment of your refusal by an expression of the warmth of your love? There must be many occasions when our prayers are in God's sight silly, impossible, ridiculous, or unwise. But the greatest heresy of all would be to think that,

---

[6] The extended humanity of Christ after his resurrection and ascension I have discussed in *A Plain Man Looks at the Cross* (Nashville: Abingdon Press, 1945).

172

as it were, he looked the other way and passed us by in icy indifference. There are unanswered prayers, but no unanswered pray-ers. And when, at long last, it may be from another viewpoint and from another plane, we can see a little more clearly the vast and yet personal plan at which God was all the time working in every human life, we shall see that justice at last is perfectly vindicated; that evil never came within miles of overcoming good, but was made to serve it; that nothing of value has, in any human sorrow or disaster, been lost; and that every member of God's human family finds his way into that unity with the eternal Spirit which is part of God's glory and the whole of man's bliss.